The Science of Science

The Science of Science

METHODS OF INTERPRETING PHYSICAL PHENOMENA

by Scientists of the Westinghouse
Research Laboratories

Russell Fox
Max Garbuny
Robert Hooke
Sharon Banigan, *Executive Editor*

A Westinghouse Search Book

WALKER AND COMPANY
NEW YORK

Contents

Foreword

THERE IS A long tradition of explaining science in generally under-
standable terms. Sir Humphry Davy, one of the great pioneers of
chemistry, was an extraordinarily popular lecturer in London a century
and a half ago. Half a century later Louis Agassiz, naturalist, geologist,
and founder of Harvard's comprehensive zoological research museum,
was as popular and as much at home in lecturing to farmers or laborers
as to students or fellow scientists. Davy and Agassiz and others like
them have wanted to explain science to the rest of the world for two
reasons. Partly, they have just wanted to share the fun. Scientists are
curious about such a lot of things; in science they find such an exciting
and rewarding kind of intellectual exercise that they just naturally
want to share with the rest of the world their excitement and pleasure
in trying to solve some of nature's puzzles.

Partly, too, there is a kind of missionary spirit. Medical, agricultural,
military, and industrial progress rest largely on a scientific base. Technology and its scientific foundations have changed man's life in so many
ways—his life span, his greater freedom from disease, the gadgets at
his disposal, the weapons that threaten him, his amusements and the
ways in which he can communicate with others, the hours he works
and the way he lives, the bases of national power and international
relations—that one either understands something about science or is
ignorant of one of the most powerful forces in the modern world.
Scientists know this and they want to help the rest of the world to
understand something of the history, the traditions, and the problems
of science and something of its principles and findings.

The scientists want to explain, and the rest of the world wants to
understand. So scientists and professional science writers have tried
a variety of means of telling the story of science. Sometimes part of

the story has been told with a kind of artificial, detective story glamour; sometimes through the biographies of famous scientists; sometimes by including bits and pieces in an account of the development of radio or the airplane or some other technological development. One strong and clear answer to the question of how science should be presented was provided by the enthusiastic public reception of the U. S. Science Exhibit at the 1962 World's Fair in Seattle, Washington. There, the story was told straight. It was the story of science, not of gadgets, or of engineering, or of medicine, or other related endeavors, but of basic science itself. It was told honestly, without being jazzed up. Thus told, it was far more popular than any industrial exhibit or any of the side shows, more popular even than the space capsule in which America's first astronaut had circled the globe. Of the 9,609,969 visitors to the fair, 6,770,109 stood in line, sometimes for hours, to see the Science Exhibit.

Of course this was not the first attempt to tell the story of science in a straightforward fashion; the lectures by Davy and Agassiz and many other efforts were of that kind. But it provided heartening evidence that there is a large audience wanting accurate, straightforward, interesting accounts of scientific work and willing to stop and do some thinking about what they are learning. The SEARCH BOOKS are part of the tradition illustrated by Davy and Agassiz and the Science Exhibit at the Seattle Fair.

There is far too much of science to cover in any one effort. Books must be written differently for the young child and the older student, for the reader who is only casually interested and the one with more serious purpose. SEARCH BOOKS are for the seriously interested student in high school or college or for the adult. Most books in the series will give these readers an understanding of modern research in a special area, such as crystals or electrons. This first one is different; it is about science as a whole and about how scientists work and think and how science is built. This is a good way to start.

DAEL WOLFLE
Executive Officer, American Association for the Advancement of Science

Preface

No SINGLE historical event will characterize the present century as much as the accelerating pace of its research activity and the technology that followed from it. Yet, for all of this, the original motivation of scientific work, its objectives and its methods, have become obscured rather than illuminated by the sheer mass and complexity of its results. Therefore, there is a growing need for a study of science as a whole, for a science behind all sciences. To be sure, this is not an entirely new discipline. What we have to say here has its roots in the ancient field of epistemology, the theory of knowledge and the methods by which it is apperceived.

In recent times, however, scientific introspection has taken a different and more creative form that by itself presents the key to important discoveries. The emphasis has shifted from abstract philosophy to the test of experience. The new aspects of scientific methods, objectives, and limitations represent the subject of our book.

RUSSELL FOX
MAX GARBUNY
ROBERT HOOKE

Pittsburgh, Pennsylvania

From Question to Question

The Purpose of Science

WHAT IS THE ultimate purpose of science? This question has challenged some of the most profound scholars of the past. It is of increasing concern today, not only to practicing research scientists but to nonscientists as well. The two groups often arrive at very different answers. This is not surprising, since the average person is influenced by the portentous consequences that science itself can engender: the launching of a manned space vehicle, or the creation of a nuclear weapon believed absurdly improbable only a decade ago. Such gigantic efforts, involving an entire nation's economic and technological resources and utilizing the skills of thousands of scientists and engineers, are widely publicized and become identified as the real purpose of scientific investigation. But any one-sided view is apt to be misleading, and this one is no exception.

How do scientists themselves regard their professional aims? When they probe the nature of matter or the structure of the universe, what is their motivation? A great majority of scientists will agree that ideally they are motivated by a compelling desire to search for truth simply as an end in itself, regardless of whether the ultimate result proves useful to mankind or disconcertingly destructive. The primary purpose of science has little to do with weapons or washing machines; it is just to know and to understand. In pursuing this objective, the scientist is guided by two complementary principles. The first is *universality*, the unlimited extension of knowledge. The second is *unification*, the linking and interrelating of information gathered from diverse sources and then attempting to explain a complexity of facts by a simplicity of causes. New observations, experiments, and theories must logically fit the established pattern of a few supreme principles, accepted as almost unassailable because no one has yet managed to disprove them.

This is the core of facts accumulated through centuries of scientific investigation.

One such time-honored principle is *causality*, the axiomatic assertion that a phenomenon occurring repeatedly under identical conditions will always have identical results, regardless of when or where it is repeated. Physics, the favorite child of natural philosophy, benefited most from this tenet and, with the ingratitude characteristic of the protégé, this same favorite child also upset the principle. We will examine this subject in more detail later, but the point to be emphasized here is that science is self-analytical and self-correcting. Not only must all new theories and observations meet the test of existing principles, but the principles themselves must constantly be subjected to re-examination. Although this process of revaluation is employed in all fields of research, it is most clearly demonstrated by the methods of the exact or measuring sciences, particularly physics, chemistry, and related fields. In these disciplines conditions can be precisely controlled, varied at will, and the effect of changes determined by a scale of numbers. In other words, it is possible not only to experiment but to measure.

In any discussion of the methods of science, physics often contributes the most representative examples. This is not because other disciplines are less rewarding, but because physics defines environmental conditions most precisely and allows the most accurate comparisons between the predictions of a theory and the facts of observation. However, when we speak of separate scientific disciplines, it is important to remember that such a division is only a convention dictated by convenience. In reality, there is no precise line where one discipline ends and another begins; instead there is a constant interchange of ideas and knowledge, with new observations and discoveries in one area often significantly influencing the others. In science, the process of unification extends across all boundaries and it is an unending task.

During the last century there has been enormous unification of an ever-growing wealth of diverse facts in physics and chemistry. For instance, various kinds and aspects of radiation—x rays, light, radio waves and their properties of propagation, reflection, scattering, and so on—although seemingly dissimilar and unconnected, have been described in terms of a single set of elementary relationships. We refer to the foundation of electromagnetic theory established by the Scottish physicist James Clerk Maxwell, whose famous equations interrelate and connect electric and magnetic fields and phenomena of radiation, thereby revealing a large part of physics as derivable from a single origin. Similarly, the theories of heat and of phenomena involving the concept of temperature in general follow, to a large extent, from two principles: the first and second laws of thermodynamics. But perhaps the greatest generality is found in the rules that govern the binding of positive and negative particles, the laws that explain what holds matter together. These concepts evolve stepwise, each model from the preceding one. First, there is the single electron and proton orbiting around each other in the hydrogen atom; from this, the model of more complex atoms; then, the characteristics of the periodic system of the elements; next, the bonding of atoms in organic and inorganic molecules; and then, most recently, the structure of the solid state with its resultant electrical, optical, and mechanical properties.

Although such examples of unification under first principles may imply a simplification of existing material, there is no indication of a reduction in the volume of science or any diminishing frontiers of research. Quite the contrary. With each newly discovered principle, other possibilities and new combinations become apparent, and as insight deepens, applications of the new knowledge leap across boundaries to attack problems that previously had defied all attempts at explanation. It was in this way that the experimental methods of physics, the advances in understanding the solid and liquid states, and parallel progress in chemistry made it possible to penetrate mysteries of biological processes such as the mechanism of heredity and mutations, the chain reactions of hormone release, and the generation and propagation of nerve impulses. Thus biophysics and biochemistry have emerged, and in turn have stimulated further advances in physiology and related fields. There is a similar interplay between the pure sciences and the practical applications such as engineering and medicine, because each stimulates and contributes to the other.

Science is a structure of many interlocking disciplines, its growth dependent on man's imagination and his compelling desire to understand his environment and himself. The basic compulsion to learn may reveal vast new horizons, end in seemingly fruitless failures, or produce agreeable or terrifying by-products, but in the long run science will fulfill its purpose. For we can say that nothing happens in nature without a reason, and the basic reason is survival of the species, which implies continuing evolution and improvement. Man's destiny is control of his environment, and the methods he employs are ultimately only a means to an end.

The Science of Methods

2

In the following pages we will describe some of the ways and means used in science to achieve the end we have just mentioned. Why is it necessary, or even possible, to say so much about scientific methods? Actually, there are two reasons.

First, the method we use to solve a given scientific problem is part of the problem itself. But because we can deal with so many questions in science by using essentially the same methods, or in other words because these methods represent a common key to all science, they are of interest in their own right. Therefore, we are concerned with the remarkable interplay between observation, reasoning, and experiment.

The second reason lies somewhat deeper. Often in the history of science, obvious inconsistencies have compelled a critical re-examination of the methods that were used to arrive at contradictory results. It is then that the most startling, even revolutionary, discoveries are made; as often as not, on such occasions man learns more about himself than about the thing he is studying. Let's see how such a situation can occur.

When we speak of atoms, electrons, or light waves—or the genes in chromosomes, for that matter—we associate these words with pictures or concepts we have formed in analogy to gross-mechanical models from our everyday experience. This is not for lack of imagination, but only because nothing else is really available to us. And such models are often surprisingly useful, and reliable within their limits. For example, we think of atoms as "planetary systems" with electrons neatly orbiting around a nucleus; but when we try to "picture" an electron or the nucleus, we find we are getting more and more hazy. Actually, what is an electron? Is it a "spherically disposed unit charge" that somehow holds together? If we continue this kind of questioning, we make the

7

horrible discovery that we actually know next to nothing about the *things themselves* whose names have become so familiar with usage. And this is true to an even greater extent when we seek reassurance in the simple, the elementary, concepts. For instance, magnetic lines of force are defined by the direction a small needle assumes in exploring a magnetic field. We can even make such lines "visible" by dusting a surface with iron filings. We also know other facts, such as that magnetic lines behave in certain ways like rubber bands. The total of such experience conveys the meaning of "lines of force." Now, as we grow confident in using this term and working with it, we become prone to an interesting confusion. Because we know some of its effects, we begin to believe that we know the thing itself. Actually, we know nothing of the sort. Just as in the case of the electron, no picture is available for magnetic force; we have no knowledge of why it can act at a distance, or of how it is propagated.

All this means that words and concepts can not only convey a meaning, but can also conceal the lack of it. Such an observation would be inconsequential except that it really lies at the root of what we have to say here. For it is on the basis of such concepts and models that the methods of research are chosen and even that the majestic structure of science is built. If we explore a phenomenon within a very narrow field of variations, we usually discover no deviation from its original concept. However, when we investigate the same thing from different viewpoints and with new methods, it may reveal entirely new and astounding qualities of itself. We say, for example, that light is a wave motion, and we prove it with experiments predicated on just such wave motion; but if we look for corpuscular behavior, we are vexed to find that light is also a stream of particles, which we call *photons*. This does not mean that natural phenomena are contradictory, but it does mean that even the most elementary things display more complicated behavior and greater dimensions than we are able to describe simultaneously with analogies from our everyday experience. Again, the theoretician can wonderfully explain and derive the behavior of a gas by the statistical accounting of its molecules, as if the laws of probability were those of marbles and holes. But his methods fail abysmally if he applies them to electrons and photons; at least, this *was* the case until he realized that the rules of the game had to be changed for these particles, and then proceeded to construct new statistics. It is obvious that it becomes impossible for anyone to say that he knows all there is to know in his field, or that all has been discovered.

Perhaps the most important reason for a critical study of methods is that it can reveal new views and directions of science, and therefore can be considered a discipline of learning. This is why we are concerned with the overlapping region that contains elements of the exact sciences, information theory, mathematics, and logic. In this sense, our subject is the science of science.

The Methods of Science

WHAT IS THE scientific method? Of course, this is a weighty philosophical subject that has been argued at length since the time of Francis Bacon. Stated in general but concise terms, particularly suitable for the experimental method, it consists of three consecutive steps:

(1) Question
(2) Test
(3) Conclusion

Any type of exploratory research can be shown to contain these elements. To illustrate the process, we will use a famous example, not because it happens to link the name of a celebrated experimentalist with that of one of the greatest theoreticians, but because it is representative of many features we will be discussing.

The end of the nineteenth century was one of those recurrent periods when it is thought that all major problems of physics have been solved, and that little is left to do but measure a few constants somewhat more accurately. In particular, at that time there was a pat answer to a question, or a group of questions, that we treat most gingerly today. By what mechanism is an electric or a magnetic field communicated from a source to a target, as from a magnet to a piece of iron? This question includes the propagation of light, which was already known to consist of electromagnetic radiation. At the time, a mechanical model represented the answer. Long-range forces, such as those corresponding to electric, magnetic, or gravitational fields, were said to be communicated as elastic stresses of an ever-present medium, "the ether." It was thought that light was simply an elastic wave carried by this same medium. The ether had to be a very special substance indeed. Some of its presumed properties implied that it might be matter, but it could not be detected by any aerodynamic resistance or the like, and obviously it did not slow down the motion of the planets. Yet presumably the ether was an all-pervading universal medium, and as such it had to be motionless.

This last postulate was of primary significance, because it established a cosmic reference system of absolute rest, against which all motion could be defined. Could such motion be proven by measurement? To answer this question, the American physicist A. A. Michelson performed an experiment, and we will use both his experiment and its consequences to demonstrate the general procedure of the scientific method.

Implicit in Michelson's experiment was the *question*, "How does the motion of the earth affect the speed of light measured on its surface?" If the earth moves through an ether at rest, an observer should indeed notice changes in the propagation velocity of light. There is a simple analogy. A stone dropped into a quiet lake generates ripples that spread as circular waves with a velocity c. Someone in a boat moving on the water with a speed v observes different velocities of the ripples, depending on the boat's navigation with respect to the wave pattern. If the boat moves exactly opposite to the direction of wave propagation, the velocity of the crests is measured as $c + v$; on the other hand, the relative velocity of the waves with respect to the boat is only $c - v$, if both are moving in the same direction. Similarly, a light signal generated in the postulated quiescent ether would propagate in it with a constant speed c. Thus, an observer moving with a velocity v in a direction opposite that of the light signal would measure a total propagation speed of $c + v$; moving along with its direction, however, he would register a speed of only $c - v$.

The *test* was conducted with an arrangement remarkable in itself as a method of experiment. The earth orbits around the sun with a velocity of about 30 kilometers per second, while the speed of light is 300,000 kilometers per second. Therefore, the effect of the earth's motion can be only very small at best. Suppose the propagation of a light signal is measured first in the direction of the earth's motion, and then perpendicular to it. To detect any alleged difference, it would be necessary in each instance to determine the velocity with an accuracy of better than one part in 10,000.

The method Michelson actually used is shown schematically in

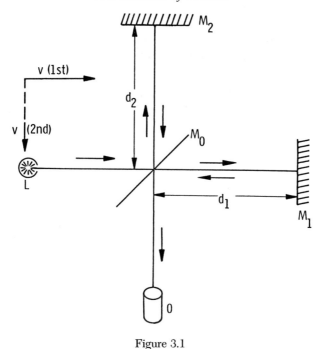

Figure 3.1

Fig. 3.1. A light beam emitted from a source L is split two ways by a partially transparent and partially reflecting mirror M_o. The two resulting light rays now proceed at right angles to each other, one in the direction of the earth's orbital motion, the other in a direction perpendicular to it. After respectively traversing the distances d_1 and d_2, the rays are reflected by the two mirrors M_1 and M_2, and return over the same distances d_1 and d_2. The rays reunite at M_o, whence they proceed together to an observing telescope O.

What is measured here in essence, but indirectly, is the *difference* between the times needed by the two light rays to travel from and to mirrors M_1 and M_2 respectively. A detailed calculation shows that if the distances d_1 and d_2 are *exactly* equal, and if the assumptions about the ether are correct, it would take a little longer for the light ray to travel in the path parallel to the earth's orbit than it would for the ray to travel perpendicular to it. The difference in these times is determined by an *interferometric* method, which will be discussed in "Space, Motion, and Time" of Part Three. As applied here, the method can be described briefly in this way: Since light consists of a wave motion, a very small time interval can be measured by the number of crests that pass a given point. In the Michelson experiment, two wave trains are superimposed in the telescope O; if these differ in time of travel, they also differ in the number of wavelengths (counted from the point at which the beam was first split). Such differences reveal themselves by a typical interference pattern of alternating dark and bright fringes, dark where the crests of one wave train coincide with the troughs of the other, and bright where crest is superimposed on crest.

Under the circumstances described, the pattern might be difficult to untangle. However, Michelson applied an important refinement. The whole apparatus (Fig. 3.1) was mounted on a revolvable platform. By rotating the arrangement 90°, first d_1 and then d_2 could be lined up with the direction of the earth's orbit. If the speed of light did vary with such a change in direction, the optical path difference between the two light beams would also be changed by the 90° rotation, and the result would be a shift in the interference pattern.

A number of salient features of Michelson's method are worth noting. First, it relies on the fact that if a signal moves one way a certain distance with a velocity $c + v$, and back again with $c - v$, the average velocity is not simply c, which would have foiled the purpose of the measurement; instead it is $c(1 - v^2/c^2)$, as a simple calculation will show. Second, it follows that a single measurement for one position of the rotary platform could, in principle, show up a difference in velocity, but this would require knowing the lengths d_1 and d_2 to an accuracy of better than one wavelength. In the actual experiment, however, when the platform was rotated the role of the two paths was interchanged with respect to the earth's motion, and therefore their differential effect was directly measured. This is perhaps one of the most perfect examples of the *zero method*, which relies on the fact that any physical quantity is more accurately determined by measuring its deviation from a known fixed value of about the same size, than by comparing it with a much smaller unit. In the present case, the method proceeds with a direct measurement of a difference $(x_1 - x_2)$ in terms of wavecrests, rather than with establishing the difference between directly measured values, x_1 and x_2.

14

Still other aspects of this test, designed to establish the effect of the earth's motion on the speed of light, may be found in more detailed treatments of the subject. However, the most famous part of Michelson's experiment is its result. *The result is negative; there is no effect.*

The *conclusion* drawn from this result is in itself a mighty theme. First of all, the fact that the interference pattern remained unchanged when the apparatus was rotated 90° could be observed repeatedly in various orientations and different positions on the earth's surface and at different times of the year, that is, when the earth's position differed with respect to the sun. Therefore, it is manifest that the speed of light is the same for all possible directions of the compass; furthermore, it is impossible by these means to establish a motion of the earth in relation to an ether at rest. This was quite an unexpected result, and it had to be explained by one of two major assumptions. We mention in passing that the cycle was thus started anew: each conclusion was based on new postulates whose consequences were again subject to test, and so dozens of subsequent experiments were spawned to settle the questions raised by the first.

One explanation, or rather a group of explanations, was conservative. It seemed necessary only to modify a little the theory of a quiescent ether, which hitherto had served so well. Michelson himself adhered to a variation called the ether drag hypothesis, which assumed that the ether, like the atmosphere, was carried along on the earth's surface. Therefore, he repeated his experiment at high altitudes between mountaintops; the result was still negative. But it is conceivable that at great altitudes the ether could be stationary with respect to the earth, and Michelson never gave up his belief that under the proper experimental conditions the ether could be demonstrated to exist. Nevertheless, whatever the explanations given in favor of this conservative view, other observations contradicted them. Here we have the situation in which a theory, originally useful and convenient in overcoming major conceptual difficulties, causes even greater difficulties in attempting to prove itself in the face of experimental counterproof, until finally it must be abandoned.

And this brings us to a most important point. Whenever an indisputable experimental result is in violent conflict with theoretical predictions, the discrepancy can often be resolved only by a radical break with long-held fundamental concepts. The explanations we have just mentioned failed to do this.

Albert Einstein saw that Michelson's results demanded critical evaluation, not of the answer but rather of the question contained in the experiment. He argued: Is it really possible to postulate a system at rest, let alone a quiescent ether, with reference to which any motion such as the earth's can be measured in absolute fashion? Is it not, in fact, impossible to determine a priori which of two systems is in motion, and which at rest? These considerations led to the basic principle of the theory of relativity: There can be no physical law that would make it possible to distinguish between various moving systems, regarding their absolute velocity or their absolute rest. Concisely stated, this was Einstein's conclusion on the basis of the ether drift experiment. At first appraisal, this statement appears innocuous and inconsequential enough. But from it follows the fact that observers on different moving systems (on different planets, for instance) would measure precisely the same speed of light. Were this not the case, it would be possible to justify a distinction between the status of motion among systems, and to establish a reference system at absolute rest. Thus, we now have two theorems, the relativistic principle and the invariance of light velocity; the combination leads to far-reaching results. For instance, there follows a relative meaning for the concepts of time and simultaneity. When we observe an event occurring during a certain time interval on an object that is moving away from us, a delay is involved in such observation because of the finite travel time of light; furthermore, the signal from the end of the event is a little more delayed than the signal from the start, because the object has moved in the interval. Thus, we should expect that a given time interval in one system is measured as a different time interval in another system. Similarly, if two events occur simultaneously in one set of coordinates, they may be observed at different times from another set.

These conclusions are not startling. What really does change the form of accepted physical laws, however, is the relativistic requirement of mutuality: Any physical magnitude (such as a length or a time interval) measured from System I on System II must assume the same value as when it is measured from System II on System I. For example, the distance d between the Eiffel Tower in Paris and the Empire State Building in New York may be measured by an astronomer on some Planet X as 3 cm shorter $(d - 3)$ than it is measured on earth. If this is the case, a distance d on Planet X will likewise be measured by an astronomer on Mount Palomar as $d - 3$. In other words, a distinction between two systems is impossible since each "views" the other with the same *distortion*.

With simple mathematics, the special theory of relativity derives a factor γ of distortion:

$$\gamma = \frac{1}{\sqrt{1 - \dfrac{v^2}{c^2}}}$$

In this equation v is the relative velocity of the two systems with respect to each other, and c is the speed of light. As the relative motion changes from $v = 0$ (at rest) to $v = c$, γ changes from 1 to ∞. Time is now distorted in the following way: Suppose a time t passes in a system moving at a velocity v with respect to us; we then observe an elapsed time γT. Thus, time is dilated; clocks on a moving object run slower.

In passing, we mention just one of the many interesting consequences of time dilation. Very energetic particles, the *cosmic rays*, come from outer space, and these produce secondary particles when colliding with the molecules of the upper atmosphere. Some of these secondaries are *mesons* which have a very short life, in fact shorter than their travel time to the earth's surface, even though they may be traveling toward earth with nearly the speed of light. Nevertheless, because of such speed their lifetime *as measured on earth* is much prolonged, and therefore they arrive before decaying. Thus, a relativistic prediction—at first much debated and contested—found experimental verification half a century later.

However, a difficulty is hidden in this last example. The mesons have an unchanged short lifetime in their own system of reference. How can this be reconciled with the observation that they arrive intact? The answer is found in the conversion factor γ, which appears also in connection with other dimensions on moving objects. Thus, the length d will be contracted to d/γ when viewed from another reference point in relative motion to the first system. From the mesons' point of view,

17

the distance they have to travel through the atmosphere is therefore reduced by the factor γ. Hence, in either case, their lifetime suffices to reach their destination; measured from the earth, their lifetime has increased, measured from the meson system, their travel time has been shortened. Either viewpoint is correct and self-consistent, since the measurements have only relative meaning.

Possibly the most important conclusions of the theory of relativity are those that involve changes in the laws of mechanics. A mass m_o when at rest, increases to $m = \gamma m_o$ when it is in motion. It should be pointed out, however, that for a large range of velocities, particularly those occurring in the macroscopic world of mechanical events, familiar in everyday experience, the relativistic mass m is not appreciably different from the *rest mass m_o*. The equation for γ shows that even if the velocity is as high as one-tenth of c (that is, for $v = 3 \times 10^9$ cm/sec), the mass has increased by only one-half per cent. Nevertheless, particles in the submicrocosm of the atoms can approach the velocity c with a corresponding gain in mass, under conditions that have now become easily observable. Of course, the speed of light c represents an unattainable upper limit for any object of finite rest mass, as the relativistic mass tends to infinity.

The most famous equation of relativity is that for E, the energy of a particle:

$$E = mc^2 = \gamma m_o c^2.$$

This is the statement of the equivalence of mass and energy, and as such it invites two kinds of experiment. First, there is the question of whether it is possible to test various forms of energy for their manifestations of mass. One such manifestation is gravity. A form of energy is light which should, therefore, have "heaviness," the word "light" notwithstanding. Indeed, the weight of light has been demonstrated experimentally by the bending of light rays from a distant star, for instance, as they pass near the sun during an eclipse; and more recently it has been shown by the loss of energy that light suffers as it moves upward against the earth's gravitational force.

The second experiment suggested by the equivalence law concerns the energy that is associated with mass. The most convincing test obviously lay in the conversion of mass into energy. The energy per gram of matter at rest is simply c^2 (ergs), which amounts to 25 billion kilowatt-hours. Right from the beginning, therefore, such conversion was expected to go over with an impressive bang.

The theory of relativity was violently contested at first and challenged for any kind of tangible proof. Half a century and many thermonuclear explosions later, the most urgently contested issue is self-restraint from any further proof.

It should now be apparent why we chose Michelson's experiment and Einstein's theory of relativity for discussion. Here is a pre-eminent example of the methods of science: The *question* arising from a hypothetical or already theoretical picture; the experimental *test;* the *conclusion* giving rise to new questions, so that the process of acquiring the results of research, knowledge, and insight moves not in circles but in a path of expanding spirals. The example is also typical as a demonstration of the inherent potential of the scientific method. Starting with a question which was basic enough, but certainly heralded no revolutionary discovery, the method proceeded under the compulsion of deductive reasoning to derive and prove such unexpected results as the heavy mass of energy and the conversion of mass into energy. However, this feat was accomplished in the final analysis by critical evaluation of the scientific method itself. In other words, a major step was taken when the theory of relativity forced the break with long-established concepts and axioms, such as the implied proposition that it is meaningful to define a universal time or a coordinate system at absolute rest. In this sense our example is more than an example; the recognition that measurements between moving systems have only a relative meaning is simply part of the science of science.

Posing the right question in science may be more difficult than finding the correct answer. To a certain extent this is also true of the subject of this book. On the face of it, our task seems simple; we just have to describe the tools of research and explain how they are used. However, if we were to do this in fact it would require many volumes, not only because there are an enormous number of individual devices, but because the underlying principles would have to be repeated over and over again. We must of necessity be selective, and therefore we will describe certain instruments not because they are most important but because they are most typical.

We will have a good deal to say about the mathematics of measurement, for measurement is science's highest court of appeal, pronouncing its final verdict for or against the meekest and the loftiest ideas alike. If the process of measurement were perfect, it could always determine at one stroke which model or theory is correct, by the simple expedient of comparing the values observed with those predicted; it could also detect precisely the slightest flaw in the agreement and thus point the way to a refinement of the model. But even the highest court of appeal can err. In common with all other observation, measurement has fundamental limitations of reliability. This is of central interest for we know that just such limitations often reveal important aspects of nature. Therefore, the accuracy of measurement must be examined, and criteria of reliability established by the procedure of statistical analysis. Measurement depends on a comparison with units and standards chosen by convention, but these can be rigidly connected to physical parameters. We plan to show that ultimately the whole of science is based on a surprisingly small number of fundamental constants, which remain unchanged in all time and space—or at least so we think.

Moreover, the critical analysis of the scientific method has a lofty final objective, and this is simply to evoke new thinking, or reveal new approaches to old problems. Such criticism has enormous potential, as we have seen, and this confronts the scientist with an unending task. But then, in science—and in good science particularly—we never reach finality. We begin with a question, and we end with a question.

Comparatively Speaking

A Standard Language

4

THE COMMUNICATION of ideas is an essential part of living. Virtually all creatures have some means of communication: the barking of a dog, for example, the song of a bird, the roar of a lion. To be sure, the message may be understood only by another of the same species. Man has evolved the most sophisticated form of communication, through the use of symbols. Symbolic signs and sounds first became identified with the objects and events they represented, and eventually this led to the development of a language. Geographic isolation in prehistoric times resulted in the development of a separate language within each tribe. Thus, a wide variety of languages came into being, each one intelligible only to a particular group of people. This confusing state of affairs has continued through the centuries, and even today we have to contend with many different languages, which makes the communication of ideas extremely difficult. Although simple ideas are easily expressed in simple language, complicated meanings or abstract ideas require a richer and more complex means of expression. There can be little doubt that many social problems stem from a misunderstanding of ideas, because of the lack of a common language with which to express them.

There are problems of communication, too, in expressing measurements. The act of making a measurement implies making a comparison. It is impossible to measure without comparing the results with something else. The statement, "Today is cold," implies that today is colder than some other days. "He is ten years old," requires a comparison of the length of time the person has lived with the number of times the earth has circled the sun. This last statement introduces another aspect of the difficulty of communicating measurement. The term "ten years old" means one thing to an American and something quite different to a Chinese, for example, since the birth date is reckoned differently in the two countries.

If we propose that the function of measurement is to develop a method for generating information, obviously the most satisfactory measurement is the one that will be useful in the widest possible variety of problems and situations. Further, of course, the means for communicating this information must be as unambiguous as possible to the largest number of people. In itself this raises the question of the proper language for the proper situation. The more complicated a language becomes, the fewer people there are who can understand it. For example, the dimensions of a brick expressed in inches or centimeters can be understood by practically everyone, but the same dimensions expressed in terms of the number of wavelengths of sodium light would have little meaning to any but a relatively small fraction of the population. Although the latter is a much more precise way to determine lengths, expressing the results in such a specialized language would be absurd when measuring bricks, since this high degree of accuracy is not required.

It is the problem of the measurer to use a language that will adequately communicate to another person the information contained in a measurement, so that he, in turn, may use this information. It is clear that since measurement entails comparisons, the standards for comparison must be useful measurements made in a wide variety of situations. Such a standard serves as the foundation of all measurement.

Every day we encounter many situations to which we pay little or no attention, because we are satisfied that they are regulated by standards. Our clothes, our food, in fact everything we buy is based on one or more standards. When we buy a gallon of paint, we are assured that the container holds a gallon of liquid and that the paint itself meets certain standards of quality. We are confident that any gasoline pump will deliver the proper number of gallons, because we know it is periodically checked against a standard, just as the butcher's scale is checked to ascertain that it weighs correctly. But this ability to buy and sell with the guarantee of fair measure is a relatively recent development in mankind's history.

In *The Story of Standards*, John Penny presents a lively picture of man's struggles to establish standards for science as well as for business.

Progress was slow in controlling standards officially in the United States. Although President Washington's first official message to Congress urged that standards be set promptly, as late as 1902 four different legal measures of length (feet) were used in Brooklyn alone. It was not until 1901 that the National Bureau of Standards was established in this country. Today this bureau sets and maintains over 700 standards of measurement and quality.

Early in his history, man realized that he needed to be able to communicate his measurements, and he developed systems of units as part of his language to facilitate his communications. Imagine a man in prehistoric times trying to describe to another the size of his cave. It is safe to guess that he accomplished this by using his own body in some way as a basic measuring unit, since even today many units are based on the human body.

Chauncey D. Leake, in his paper *Standards of Measurement and Nursery Rhymes,* describes the evolution and history of some of our modern units of measurement. Records go back to ancient Egypt, but in describing the Egyptian system we will use the more familiar equivalents of Greek, Latin, and Anglo-Saxon origin. According to Dr. Leake's presentation, the earliest known system for short lengths, based on parts of the human body, was obtained by doubling or halving fundamental units. The smallest unit was the finger—one *digit.* Doubling this, one obtained two digits, equal to *half a hand.* Logically enough, two half-hands equaled *one hand;* even today we measure the height of a horse in terms of hands. Two hands were a *span,* and two spans equaled a *cubit,* which was also the distance from finger tips to elbow. Two cubits were an *arm,* measured from chin to finger tips, and equivalent to our yard. Two arms were a *fathom.*

For longer distances, it was more convenient to use the *step* or *pace.* The early Egyptians apparently noticed that three feet were roughly equal to one arm. Two steps, measured heel to toe, equaled the extended arms. This *double step* was a unit, and a hundred double steps was one *stade,* equivalent to two hundred yards. The stade was also a unit of measurement in ancient Greece, and was used in their Olympic foot races. The amphitheater, originally designed for these races and called the *stadion,* later became known as the Roman *stadium.* Ten stades was the Roman mile.

The human body was also used as a basis for volume measure. One fairly reproducible volume was the mouthful, and the Egyptians seem to have started with the *mouthful* as a unit. This was the *ro*, and it was represented graphically by a hieroglyphic symbol shaped like a mouth. The system of doubling was also employed for volume measurement. Two mouthfuls were one *handful* or *jigger;* two handfuls equaled a *jack* or *jackpot;* two jacks were a *jill* (or gill); two jills, a *cup;* two cups, a *pint* or *jug;* two pints, a *quart;* two quarts, a *pottle;* two pottles, a *gallon;* two gallons equaled a *pail,* and two pails, a *peck;* two pecks were one *bushel;* two bushels, a *strike.* Two strikes were a *coomb;* two coombs, a *cask;* two casks equaled one *barrel,* and two barrels, a *hogshead;* two hogsheads, a *pipe,* and two pipes, a *tun.* Of course, many of these terms are familiar to those of us who use the English system of units.

It was not only quite easy but fairly common for people to cheat in measuring volume, because it was difficult to check the exact sizes of the containers used. In fact, during the seventeenth century, when King Charles the First of England taxed the jackpot, the people expressed their vexation in a popular rhyme, which has survived to this day as the familiar nursery rhyme, *Jack and Jill.* The quaint term "jackpot" has survived, too, used primarily in gambling circles.

When it came to standard weight, the human body was obviously inadequate as a basic unit. However, the Egyptians recognized that kernels of wheat were extremely uniform, and the *grain* was adopted as one of the earliest units of weight. Scale balances in a variety of sizes are known to have been used in Egypt as early as 4000 B.C. And even today pharmaceuticals are measured in grains.

The first units of time were undoubtedly associated with the apparent motion of the sun. Observing the moving shadow of a stick or rock, man contrived the first crude means for dividing the day into smaller units. Ancient shadow clocks led to sundials, and these became more and more complicated, even including marks to allow for changes in the year. The need to tell time on cloudy days and to transport the device more easily led to the invention of the sand "hourglass" and later water clocks and candle clocks.

In establishing all these units, man was gradually devising ways of communicating his measurements. Of course, it became increasingly obvious that units were not enough. When the ancient trader was buying or selling an arm of cloth, he naturally questioned whose arm was to be used for measuring it. Again the early Egyptians seem to have thought of an answer to the problem by using the "royal arm" as a standard. But each new ruler meant a new standard, and if there happened to be a quick succession of rulers, there was some doubt about which royal arm was considered standard. As traders began to travel from one country to another, the difficulties compounded. It is easy to imagine the inevitable confusion at a large center of world trade, when merchants from many different countries tried to arrive at standard values.

As late as the nineteenth century, four different measures of volume were used in the United Kingdom; the peck varied sufficiently between England, Scotland, Ireland, and Wales to make it profitable for a trader to buy long in one country and sell short in another. This situation, and others equally confusing in various countries, led to agitation for uniform standards. Because the British were among the most successful merchants when this agitation was at its height, the British system was widely adopted and is still used extensively throughout the world.

Toward the end of the eighteenth century, the French Revolution brought about many reforms, one of which was a new system of weights and measures. But the French had not been under the strong British influence experienced in the American colonies, and instead of adopting the English system, the French tackled the problem logically and soundly. They saw the possibility of establishing a relationship between volume measurement, linear measurement, and mass or weight, by reference to a single basic standard, linear measurement. The same idea, incidentally, had also occurred to the early Egyptians; they felt that a standard length could be converted to a standard volume, and when the volume was filled with water, for example, it could in turn serve as a standard of weight.

Initially the French thought that a standard length, used as a simple pendulum, might also serve as a standard for time. However, this idea was abandoned when they realized that time would differ in various parts of the world because of a variety of effects, such as the flattening of the earth at the poles, changes in elevation, and the effects of the earth's angular velocity.

27

After much deliberation, the French Commission arbitrarily decided to adopt as the standard for linear measurement one ten-millionth of the distance from the earth's poles to the equator. This length, called the *meter,* became the basis of the metric system. For the standard meter, a bar of platinum-iridium was chosen, because of its minimal coefficient of expansion. This bar is still carefully kept at constant temperature and humidity in the Paris Institute for Weights and Measures. A cube, each of whose sides equals the standard length, was adopted as a basis for standard volume, and one-thousandth of this volume became the *liter.* The mass of one cubic centimeter of pure water at 4° centigrade (the point of maximum density) served to define a *gram.* A mass of pure platinum equal to 1,000 standard grams became the standard *kilogram,* and this, too, is kept in the Institute.

Because the metric system uses multiples of tens, which simplifies measurement operations, scientists immediately recognized its merits and adopted this system as the standard of scientific measurements. In the United States, the metric system was made legal in 1866, identifying the English system in terms of the metric system. However, both systems are widely used now, even in scientific circles. Most physicists and chemists prefer the metric system, while engineering measurements are frequently expressed in English units. A conference of physicists and engineers often becomes a scene of frantic calculations, as everybody tries to convert, for example, from BTU's per pound of fuel for pounds per square inch of thrust, to calories per gram for dynes per square centimeter. It takes only one such conference, or a glance at the conversion tables in any handbook, to get an idea how much time, space, and energy are wasted because of a lack of standardization among people who measure the same quantity.

The most important principle to recognize about standardization is that it does not matter what the standard is, as long as everybody agrees that it *is* the standard. For example, it makes no difference whatever whether the meter bar in Paris is actually one ten-millionth of the distance from the pole to the equator, which incidentally it is not, or whether it is one million wavelengths of sodium light, which also it is not. The important point is that there is complete agreement that the distance between two scratches on a particular platinum-iridium bar defines the meter. All other measurements can then be referred to this unit, thus providing a universal standard so that when a distance of 10.00 meters is specified, everyone knows precisely what is meant.

If we were concerned only with measuring the fundamental constants —mass, length, and time—the system of units we adopted would be of little significance. However, our measurements are often not that simple. Although all measurements except temperature can ultimately be reduced to these three fundamental constants, it is not always apparent that this is true. It can be seen that velocity is distance per time, hence $\dfrac{\text{L(ength)}}{\text{T(ime)}}$, or that force is mass multiplied by acceleration, and therefore

$$\frac{\text{M(ass)} \times \text{L(ength)}}{\text{T(ime)}^2} = \frac{ML}{T^2}$$

Also, work is defined as a force F acting through a distance L, so

$$\text{work} = FL = MaL = \frac{ML^2}{T^2},$$

where a is the acceleration. However, in measuring electricity the situation quickly becomes confused, because of the ways we have chosen to define electron current and electric charge. In the earliest studies of electricity, experiments were concerned with electrostatic charges. The electric charge was defined in terms of the force between two charges q_1 and q_2 in a vacuum, by means of the law

$$F = \frac{q_1 q_2}{d^2},$$

where d, the distance between charges, is a length of quantity L. Thus, if $q_1 = q_2 = q$, then $q = d\sqrt{F}$ or generally $q = L\sqrt{F}$. Now, since

$$F = \frac{ML}{T^2}, \quad q = \frac{M^{1/2}L^{3/2}}{T}$$

But if the measurements are not done in a vacuum, we have to add a constant k, called the *dielectric constant*, depending on the nature of the medium in which the charges are suspended. However, the last equation above defines the unit charge in the *electrostatic system* if M, L, and T are expressed in grams, centimeters, and seconds respectively.

With the discovery of the Faraday effect, that an electrical conductor moving in a magnetic field induces an electric current, a new means was needed for defining the unit of electricity. Most of the measurements dealt with electrical currents (moving electric charges) and hence the definition was in terms of the force between two infinitely long parallel wires carrying the currents i_1 and i_2. Since the currents produce magnetic fields, the definition was based on the force between unit magnetic poles, in a manner analogous to that used for electrostatic charge. This *electromagnetic* unit of charge can be shown to be equal to

$$q = M^{1/2}L^{1/2} \qquad \text{for vacuum,}$$

and
$$\frac{M^{1/2}L^{1/2}}{\sqrt{\mu}} \qquad \text{for other media.}$$

If we equate these two units of charge, we have

$$\frac{k^{1/2}M^{1/2}L^{3/2}}{T} = \frac{M^{1/2}L^{1/2}}{\mu^{1/2}}.$$

For this equality to be true, $\sqrt{k\mu} = T/L$, which is the reciprocal of velocity. This velocity has been shown to be that with which electromagnetic waves are propagated in the medium. So we have the ratio of the electromagnetic unit of charge to an electrostatic unit of charge equal to the velocity of light, or 3×10^{10} cm/sec.

In the more recently developed MKS (meters, kilograms, seconds) system of units, this confusing situation has been avoided by adopting a fourth dimension, the unit of electrical charge. Extreme care is needed to express electrical measurements in the proper system of units, because frequently a measurement of electric and magnetic fields involves both electrostatic and electromagnetic units.

At present there is not universal agreement about the best system for expressing the physical units, and in some respects modern physics has confused the issue rather than solved the problem. There has been a tendency to introduce a new unit every time a new problem arises. For example, in nuclear physics the unit of length is called the *fermi* (10^{-13} centimeters), and the *barn* is the unit of area (10^{-24} square centimeters). But since the two units were introduced independently, there is no logical connection between them. To add to the confusion, the fermi is named for the physicist Enrico Fermi, but since he invented the term "barn" for the unit of area, some physicists refer to this unit as the fermi. This is an intolerably confusing practice.

Many units used only by special groups have come into being, and this compounds the confusion and duplication. Several systems have been proposed to eliminate ambiguous terms and establish a more modern and logical system related to the atom. The idea is sound and certainly has merit, but it will take many years of conferences and discussions before such a change can be effected.

However, while these matters are annoying, they are of secondary importance compared to the definitions. After all, it is not important what a unit is called, as long as it is defined in the same way by everybody. When there is doubt about the name, such as *newton, weber, gauss,* or *oersted,* the proper dictionary or handbook can clarify the issue. What is most important is that a newton in France, England, Germany, or any other country, represents the same physical quantity for measurements. Measurement has meaning only if we can transmit the information without ambiguity to others.

Why Measure?

5

History fails to record a case in which the subject of weights and measures was greeted with cries of delight by students. In fact, only human inertia and a lack of alternatives prevent mass exodus from physics courses when this topic is introduced, saving us from a consequent scarcity of physicists all over the world. Why, then, do we expect more than a peculiar minority to read a discourse on measurement?

To begin with, our subject is measurement as it affects science and our understanding of nature, rather than just an accumulation of our technical knowledge. An architect planning a skyscraper relies on a number of measurements that he finds in a handbook. These figures, important as they are to the architect and to the future inhabitants of his creation, are of no interest in themselves. Science provides an essential service to technology in producing measurements, and instruments for obtaining them, which are important in making our machines, buildings, roads, bridges, and missiles perform their proper functions. Such measurements, however, are not the concern of this book. Rather we shall explore some of the ways in which the measurement process is related to our basic knowledge of nature.

Imagine a time before the thermometer was invented. People spoke of "hot" and "warm" and "cold," and they could say that ice is colder than steam, or that Arabia is warmer than Norway. If asked, "How much warmer?" they would have given a variety of answers, such as, "a little," or "a great deal," or even, "who knows?" A philosophical person might have answered with a lecture on the impossibility of measuring such a subjective quantity.

After all, he might have said, in the first place, there is no yardstick. Nor is there likely to be, since the thing is not additive in the usual way.

You may add 5 feet (or pounds, or minutes) to 3 feet (or pounds, or minutes) and you get 8 feet (or pounds, or minutes). But if you add a bucket of hot water to a bucket of still hotter water, the result is hotter than the former but not as hot as the latter. Furthermore, the whole matter depends on the observer. Yesterday seemed a hot day to me, but to you it may have seemed cool. Certainly the Swahili and the Eskimo have different ideas on the subject. No, this is just not a quantitative matter, and it is no more susceptible to measurement than are beauty, courage, honesty, or intelligence.

Think how the idea of a thermometer changes our ideas about the nature of temperature. It is not just that we can attach a number to various degrees of warmth. More importantly, scientists can study the properties of heat and heat transfer and can communicate their results in terms that can be mutually understood. It is interesting to speculate about the phenomena we now consider hazy, intangible, or subjective that will be easily measured quantitatively a hundred years from now.

One objective of measurement, then, is to make communication possible. When a result can be expressed numerically, it can be transmitted to others.

Another objective is to provide deeper understanding of the phenomena being measured. To illustrate, consider one of the many quantities which are being measured today by means of instruments that produce results of uncertain value. An intelligence test is an instrument that measures something and produces a number. Applied several times to the same subject, such tests produce results that are distressingly variable. There is also the big question as to what it is that is being measured. This question naturally leads us to wonder what intelligence is. Yet as "better" tests are devised, more will be learned about the subject, and there will be increasing agreement on the question of what the tests are measuring.

Superficial study of the physical sciences leads some people to believe that physical measurements do not pose the problems that are raised by psychological and sociological measurements. Yet whenever physical measurements are pushed to the limits of their precision, or to the ends of the range in which they work, all the same problems appear. It seems more realistic to believe that the measurements of the physical sciences differ from those of other disciplines only in degree. *All* measurements are approximations, and it is generally not possible to state *exactly* what they are measuring.

Take, for example, measures of length, perhaps the simplest type of all. Suppose we have a small package to mail, and we know that the mailbox will accommodate packages up to 12″ in length. All we have to do is to apply a ruler to the package, measuring its length. If the answer is 11″, we can be sure that the package can be mailed; if it is 13″, we can be sure that it cannot. This kind of thing has been done for thousands of years and seldom leads to any philosophizing. But if our measurement is 12″, we are in doubt. What is the source of such doubt? Experience says that the package may or may not go through the slot. The problem can be temporarily solved by measuring in small fractions of an inch, but eventually we are up against the question, "What *is* the length of an object?" Even a piece of polished steel has its rough edges, though we may need a microscope to see the roughness. Possibly the definition of the length of such a piece (Fig. 5.1) should be the distance between the dotted lines which are perpendicular to the axis of the bar and which just touch the outermost projections. This does not solve the problem, however, for the roughness along the long edges of the bar prevents the exact determination of the axis. Furthermore, if we could carry our measurements to a precision corresponding to the molecular level, we would find that our rough edges are in motion, making all earlier problems seem trivial.

In other words, whether we try to measure a "simple" characteristic such as length, or a complex one such as intelligence, thoughtful application of the measurement process forces us to ask what it is that we are trying to measure, and this question often leads to deeper knowledge than we had before.

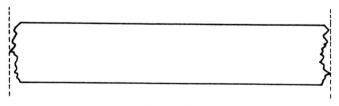

Figure 5.1

A third objective of measurement is to provide verifications of theories, or selections from groups of theories. Suppose, for example, that an astronomical measurement formerly believed to be 1.34278 is discovered to be actually 1.34276. By itself, this is scarcely front-page news. However, if one number was predicted by Newtonian physics and the other by a newcomer named Einstein, the difference could be most exciting. The theories of Newton and Einstein are qualitatively poles apart. For our understanding of the universe, it is therefore crucial to know which comes closer to an accurate description of the state of nature. Quantitatively, however, the two differ so little that the question can be resolved only by very accurate measurement made on an astronomical scale, so that at such times we must thoroughly understand the measurement process in order to make progress.

Speaking of progress, we might even claim, as a fourth objective of measurement, that numerical description is an inherent necessity for evaluation of progress. Do music, art, or understanding of history progress? They certainly change, but the changes are always assessed as positive by some and negative by others. We can assert that there are runners today who can run the mile faster than anyone could fifty years ago, but who can produce evidence that today's boxers or wrestlers are better than those of previous generations? The difference is in measurement.

Unmeasured activities tend to be subject to fads and fashions. Unable to establish any evidence of real improvement, people tend to make changes for the sake of variety, and often a periodic effect sets in, as in the lengths of women's skirts. It would be obtuse to claim that even science is free of such irrational ups and downs. For example, there are theories between which science has oscillated (e.g., wave nature versus particle nature of light), but when a stand is taken which has been occupied and abandoned in the past, it is usually as a result of the acquisition of new numerical information.

Finally, there is the possibility always that we are not measuring the "right" thing, whatever that may be. The fact that our measurements are quantitative and "scientific" does not necessarily mean that we are measuring what we should be measuring. In other words, although measurement seems to be necessary in order to provide landmarks for progress, progress itself is not an easy concept to describe. For example, it was stated above that there are runners today who can run faster than anyone could fifty years ago. We have measurements to prove this, but we should not necessarily conclude, for example, that human beings are faster. The difference may be due to improved equipment, improved tracks, more people trying (the best of a large population usually beats the best of a smaller one), and so on. The mere fact that we can record times does not answer all questions, does not define progress, and does not necessarily measure the kind of progress that we think it does; but such measurement is nevertheless by far our best weapon against prejudiced opinion.

Some Facts

6

IN THE preceding chapter we set up something of an idol of numerical measurement; in this chapter we shall follow the scientific custom of inspecting its feet for signs of clay.

We have expressed a preference for statements such as, "Light travels at 186,000 miles per second," over such statements as, "Light travels at a fantastic speed." In a careless moment one might defend this preference by declaring that the former statement is "exact." It is not, of course, as the three zeros in the figures 186,000 testify. These zeros (or similar ones farther down the line, if we put in all the significant figures that we know) are not legitimate mathematical digits, but merely monuments to our ignorance. Over the years we learn more and more digits in this figure, but there always remain more we have not learned, and there is a fringe area between known and unknown where we are uncertain and our measurements disagree.

Some may feel that there is no problem so long as our measurements agree as closely as we need for "practical" purposes. Yet we have already made it clear that our concern here is not only for things that appear to be practical. The questions Einstein raised about Newtonian mechanics were not of a practical nature. (The fact that times have changed and that some of these considerations may be quite practical to astronauts of the future does not change the fact that Einstein was not motivated by practicalities.) Therefore, we cannot always drag in practicality to help us answer the question, "What is a measurement, particularly when we cannot measure the same thing twice and get the same answer?"

A butcher does not measure slices of meat with a micrometer, and it is generally considered unnecessary to use chemical balances for weighing a baby. In other words, the most sensitive instruments are reserved for the jobs where they are needed, and cruder ones are used for cruder measurements; in fact, the sensitive instrument may be altogether inadequate for the crude job, as in the baby-weighing case. The gist of all this is that normally a measuring instrument is used near the limits of its ability. Moreover, in scientific work, often the most precise instrument in existence is not quite so precise as we should like it to be.

These facts contribute to "measurement error," a phenomenon which every user of instruments should try to understand. Not only does it affect his individual measurements, but it is also closely related to the philosophy of what he is trying to do and often to the real meaning of his work.

"Measurement error" is a phrase we use to refer to the fact that repeated measurements of "the same thing" are usually different. Unfortunately, the word "error," which covers all such variability, tends to imply incompetence. The implication of incompetence can make some insecure scientists pretend that they are free from error, and serious trouble may result, since measurement error is almost universal. Given a small bag of marbles, several people can count the contents and be reasonably sure of coming up with the same answer. This is about as complicated as a situation can become and still be essentially free of measurement error. In other cases the error, though it may be small even to the point of being unimportant, is nevertheless there, and we cannot tell whether it *is* small until we learn something about it.

Every measuring instrument has some clear limitation which is related to the smallest unit that appears on its scale. For example, if a ruler is marked off in inches, and the inches into tenths of inches, one may guess hundredths of an inch between two adjacent markings. This is as far as it is reasonable to go, and it is clear that this instrument presents an error of about .01″ as a result of the nature of its scale. The ruler's sensitivity in this respect is sometimes called its *resolution*.

It is our sad duty to point out that there are some scientists who, when asked for an estimate of their error, report only the error that is due to an instrument's lack of resolution. These people have much to learn.

What are some of the other sources of measurement error? We have said that by error we mean the variation among repeated measurements of the "same thing." The principal source of trouble is that when two measurements are made, they must occur at different times or at different places, or both. At these times or places,

(a) the "same thing" may not be quite the same, which is why we have used the quotation marks;

(b) the instrument may undergo slight changes, or there may even be two instruments used;

(c) the user of the instrument may change, or the same person's use of the instrument may differ a bit from one measurement to the next;

(d) the circumstances surrounding the measurement may change. (Changes such as in temperature or in humidity probably affect the error through changes induced in the thing measured, the instrument, its user, or more than one of these.)

We may conclude from this analysis that the way to minimize error is to make our measurements as nearly simultaneous as possible. It is true that in this way we tend to produce relatively consistent results. Results observed at almost the same time in almost the same place, however, may tell us little or nothing about what will happen at other times and places. Therefore, since the time will never return, and the place may be of little interest, such results are apt to be of dubious value. Spreading observations out over time and place introduces more "error," but it also permits a more universal application of results.

So much for the sources of measurement error. What are its effects? Unfortunately, they are often all too clear. In much the way that a solar eclipse confuses the natives of a remote Pacific atoll, measurement error can confuse the observer who does not understand it. We all like constancy for its comforting predictability. Uncertainty is unpleasant, for it upsets our plans. If we make two supposedly identical measurements which turn out to be 3.24 and 3.27, we are faced with a problem. Which one is "right"? Is either one "right"? What, in fact, do we mean by "right"? What is the next measurement likely to be?

There are those, it must be admitted, who run away from this problem by resolving never again to take a second measurement. Truth lies in the opposite direction, of course, as we will now try to explain.

Measurement Error—An Approach to its Treatment

When we measure the same thing several times, the measurements we obtain are representative of a large family of measurements that might be produced if we were to take measurements indefinitely under these circumstances. Once we admit the existence of this large family of measurements, it becomes clear that the problem of measurement is to specify this family.

To illustrate, suppose that we decide to measure the temperature of boiling apple juice. We put the juice in a pan, heat it until it boils, and take its temperature. Contrary to popular belief, what we have done does not constitute "the scientific method," but only a small part of it. The important parts of the scientific method are the selection of experiments to perform and the interpretation of the results obtained.

Why did we decide to measure the boiling point of apple juice? At the technological level, presumably we did so to obtain a result that other people want, and the result is published to prevent duplication of effort all over the world and in future years. At the scientific level, we did so presumably to learn more about the nature of the substance. In either case, the big question is, "To what future situations does our result have any relevance?"

The experiment should be regarded not merely as an effort to obtain a particular temperature reading, but as the larger effort of finding what this reading means. Usually this necessitates repeating the experiment; this is the only way to find out if our observation will be seen again in future experiments, and to what extent. When we repeat the experiment, should we use the same juice again? The same pan? The same rate of heating? These are important questions. If we never change the pan, there is no evidence *in the experiment* that what we have learned applies to any other pan, and the same is true for the juice, the heat rate, and other factors that could be named. Intuition or experience tells us that the influence of the pan is negligible, if it is uncovered. Such intuition must always be used, since in all cases there are hundreds of factors that are too obviously irrelevant to be worth investigating. On the other hand, we must be careful, lest our intuition tell us that a result obtained in Boston is valid in Denver; our existing knowledge happens to include the fact that altitude affects boiling points, but someone had to discover this the first time.

When an experiment is repeated, then, some circumstances should be changed and some should not. What the experimenter does in this connection is crucial, since it determines the scope of situations to which the experiment is relevant.

Apple juice was deliberately selected for this illustration because there is really no point in making a very careful measurement of the boiling point of a batch of juice; the next batch will boil at a different temperature. Two apples will not contain the same amount of sugar, for example, and neither will their juice. The boiling point of a chemically pure liquid, such as water or mercury, can be communicated to a scientist anywhere, since he can duplicate this pure liquid (almost) and check the result; such a result is therefore usually more important scientifically than the results obtained for a poorly defined substance.

In summary, this example has illustrated the following points:

1. The quantity A to be measured should be something that can be specified and duplicated elsewhere. (Unless, of course, the measurement concerns only a specific object or event, and is made with no intention of producing knowledge about any similar objects or events. This case is more common in carpentry than in science.)

2. Certain circumstances are kept under control (e.g., the altitude in the boiling experiment), so that the experiment can be described as the measurement of A under circumstances B.

3. Other circumstances will, in all cases, be left uncontrolled. These help to cause the measurement error, and the effect of these uncontrolled circumstances C is revealed by taking repeated measurements. The effect of C should be small. If it is not small enough for the purposes of the measurement, then a study must be made in order to reveal which uncontrolled circumstances are producing major effects and must be controlled and therefore put into B.

With these points in mind, we can look at a certain measurement situation and state that in measuring A under circumstances B, there is a "population" of measurements in which we are interested; this population is the set of all measurements that could conceivably be made as the uncontrolled circumstances C are allowed to vary. We can think of a large number of scientists in varying parts of the world, measuring A over and over again under circumstances B and sending their results to a central office. After some time we would expect the collection of numbers at the central office to become somewhat stable. That is, this collection would grow in size, but not in "shape," in the sense that the fraction of reported measurements between 3.18 and 3.19, say, would settle down and remain fairly steady. The steady state is the thing we wish to describe.

It would be very desirable to have a better definition of a population than this. The concept is not a mathematical one, however, and does not seem to be susceptible to precise description. In the purely mathematical treatment of our problem, we do not need this description; it really serves only to explain the relevance of the mathematics to a physical situation.

Assuming that we have some conception of a population of possible measurements, we see that a few measurements actually made in an experiment are a sample from this population. A sample is a certain kind of selection of members of a population, and is illustrated by the selection of a group of people by an opinion poll to provide information about the opinions of the entire population of the country. The population is the set of all such measurements, and the sample is the subset of measurements made on the selected group of people. Here a measurement need not be a number, but could, for example, be the answer to the question, "Do you favor higher tariffs?"

The problem of estimating the characteristics of a population by observing a sample is the central problem of the subject of mathematical statistics. This process of *inference*, as it is sometimes called, is also a fundamental one in experimental science, since the scientist looks at a few observations and infers or tries to generalize correctly to a much larger family of possible (or future) observations.

Statistics is too large a subject to cover here; it is not even possible to discuss the prevalent misconceptions about it. We must, however, present a few important points in order to show the relationship to measurement.

Imagine a small island whose adult male population numbers 60, and suppose that we are interested in providing these men with trousers so that they will be able to appear in public after they learn about modesty. We are interested in their waist measurements, and, though we do not know it, the population can be specified as in Fig. 6.1.

				29							
				29							
			28	29	30						
			28	29	30						
			28	29	30	31					
		27	28	29	30	31					
		27	28	29	30	31	32				
		27	28	29	30	31	32				
	26	27	28	29	30	31	32	33			
25	26	27	28	29	30	31	32	33	34		
24	25	26	27	28	29	30	31	32	33	34	35	38

Distribution of waist measurements (in inches) in population of 60 men.

Figure 6.1

This shows that there is one man whose waist measures 24″, 11 with 29″ waists, and so on. The chief, who has never done any work, stands somewhat apart from the commoners, as is his custom.

Persuading a suspicious and ticklish savage to stand still and have his waist measured is an operation we do not care to repeat any more times than necessary, so we wonder if we can learn what we need to know by taking a sample.

The population of Fig. 6.1, though smaller than populations usually studied in practice, will serve as an example for explaining the idea of sampling. A sample is a small subset of a population taken to provide information about the population, such as a drop of blood taken by a doctor to learn about a patient's entire supply, or a glass of water used by a chemist to study the purity of a water system. In order to learn how samples provide information about populations, we naturally study samples from known populations. For example, suppose we put each number from Fig. 6.1 on a separate slip of paper, put all the slips into a hat, mix well, and draw out, say, 10 of them. The result could be something like this:

27, 34, 25, 28, 27, 27, 31, 34, 29, 38.

At first glance, there seems to be very little in this sample to suggest the nature of the parent population. Even if we arrange the sample as we arranged the population, there still is no discernible "shape" as there was in Fig. 6.1:

```
27
27                        34
25    27 28 29    31       34              38
```

Figure 6.1a

Fortunately, the sample does contain information about the shape of the population, and it is one of the jobs of mathematical statistics to dig out whatever information is present. One much used procedure is to suppose that the population shape is described by some equation involving one or more unknown constants (called parameters) and then use the sample to estimate the appropriate values of the parameters. For example, the most commonly occurring shape is described by the *normal,* or *Gaussian, distribution,* which is represented by a certain bell-shaped curve. This curve is defined by the equation

$$y = \frac{1}{\sigma \sqrt{2\pi}} \, e^{-(x-\mu)^2/2\sigma^2}.$$

Here e is the base of the "natural logarithms," $e = 2.71828 \ldots$, and x and y are variables referring to a coordinate system. The quantities μ (mu) and σ (sigma) are parameters that determine, respectively, the location and the shape of the curve. For the data of Fig. 6.1, the best values for μ and σ^2 are 29.5 and 6.73, respectively; these values produce the curve in Fig. 6.1b, providing a fair description of the population.

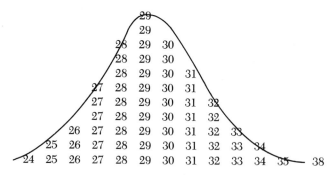

Figure 6.1b

In practice, we do not know the best values of μ and σ^2 and we must estimate them from a sample. The question is, "What does a sample provide that tells us that $\mu = 29.5$ and $\sigma^2 = 6.73$, at least approximately?" This question is answered for various cases under the heading of "estimation of parameters," a central problem of statistics. We will illustrate a simple case here.

In the equation describing the normal distribution, μ represents the mean of the population, while σ^2 is the "variance," or mean square deviation from the mean. When we have a sample as in Fig. 6.1a, then, we estimate μ by taking the arithmetic mean or the average of the numbers in the sample. Since these 10 numbers are 25, 27, 27, 27, 28, 29, 31, 34, 34, and 38, our estimate of μ becomes 300/10, or 30. The deviations from this mean are

$$-5, -3, -3, -3, -2, -1, 1, 4, 4, 8,$$

the squares of which are

$$25, 9, 9, 9, 4, 1, 1, 16, 16, 64,$$

adding to 154. The mean square deviation from the mean is therefore found by dividing 154 by the appropriate number, which turns out to be not 10, but 9. (Division by one less than the sample size happens to just cancel, on the average, the bias introduced by the fact that the deviations are calculated from the sample mean rather than the population mean.) Thus our estimate of the variance is 17.1, illustrating the fact that variances are not very well estimated by small samples. Using

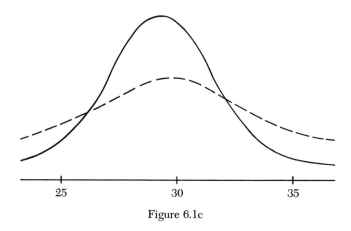

Figure 6.1c

the estimates of 30 for μ and 17.1 for σ^2, together with tables of the normal distribution, we would arrive at the dotted curve of Fig. 6.1c, shown with the curve (solid line) which appeared previously in Fig. 6.1b.

A larger sample, of course, would usually provide a closer result. Everyone knows this, and the general public invokes something called "the law of averages" to explain it. A sizable body of mythology has grown up around this law. Some seem to think that it describes an actual physical restoring force, believing that a coin that has come up heads five times in a row is very likely to come up tails on the next throw; actually, the chances are even again, if the coin is of natural dimensions.

To illustrate another fallacy, the average layman is disturbed at the thought of trying to learn something about the population of the United States by looking at a sample of size 2,000, say. Yet he may feel that 2,000 is much more than necessary to learn about a city whose population is 50,000. The fact is that if we take a sample of size n from a population of size N, the sample mean will vary from sample to sample, and the variance of this sample mean will describe the amount of information the sample provides about the mean. If σ^2 is the population variance and σ_m^2 stands for the variance of the sample mean m, it can be shown that

$$\sigma_m^2 = \frac{\sigma^2}{n}\left(1 - \frac{n}{N}\right).$$

In the two cases just mentioned, $n = 2,000$ and N is 185,000,000 (for the United States) or 50,000 (for a city). In these two cases

$$\sigma_m^2 = .000499995\ \sigma^2$$

and $$\sigma_m^2 = .00048\ \sigma^2,$$

respectively, and the difference between these two results is of no importance whatsoever. Only when the sample size reaches a substantial fraction of the population size does the size of the population have any bearing on the question.

At least as important as the sample size is the question of how the sample was obtained. We have not said very much about sampling procedure except to define it in terms of slips of paper in a hat. This is not always feasible, and, besides, it only illustrates without telling what the basic elements of the procedure are. To be more general, we say that a simple random sample of size n from a population of size N is one so chosen that

(a) at the beginning, and after each selection, the remaining members of the population have equal probabilities of being selected; or, equivalently,

(b) each group of n members of the population has the same probability of constituting the sample as each other group of size n.

This definition does not cover the case of sampling from infinite populations, but that is a story for much more detailed treatments of probability and statistics.

In the language that has been introduced, the quantitative study of measurements is carried out by supposing that a group of measurements actually obtained is a sample from a population of measurements that might have been obtained. This population is usually only a concept, or an abstraction, as are the straight lines without width in geometry, for example. It is not easy, in any given case, to describe the population about which we are trying to learn something. Unless we attempt to define this population, however, we do not know where we are going, and consequently we certainly do not know how to get there.

Measurement and the "Scientific Method"

Although measurement is only a part of experimentation, the problem of interpreting measurements is about the same as the larger problem of interpreting experiments. The interpretation of experimental results, or of measurements, is difficult because the problem is inductive, rather than deductive. Inductive reasoning consists of the observation of certain events until one feels safe in deciding that future events will follow the same pattern. Deductive reasoning starts with certain assumed (or "self-evident") axioms and determines the inevitable consequences.

Science uses both types of reasoning, of course, and progress in science is made by a succession of steps of both kinds. If we should look into the process at the time when an experiment is in progress, for example, we might observe the following sequence of events. The experiment produces certain results. These are studied and used to conjecture (inductive reasoning) what will happen in future cases. Meanwhile, results from this and other experiments are combined and a general "theory" is suggested to explain them. This theory may depend on certain fundamental assumptions or suppositions, from which (by deductive reasoning) we can determine that certain consequences must follow. It is often easy to propose a theory that fits the observations already made, but the true test of the theory is its capacity to suggest further experiments and predict their results. When such experiments are performed they help check the validity of the assumptions of the theory. Now we are where we came in, and the cycle repeats itself.

Here we are interested in the measurement problem, and therefore in reasoning of the inductive type. Anyone who has survived the uncertainties of this world for as long as ten or fifteen years does not need to have pointed out to him the vagaries of inductive reasoning. Many very ancient proverbs attest to man's unhappy experiences in this direction: "One swallow does not a summer make," and "Einmal ist keinmal," which is German for, "One time is no time at all," and so on.

How, then, can science justify the use of such reasoning, and how can we reduce its dangers? The justification comes from results. We use inductive reasoning constantly, because we have to, and we know from experience that it is valuable to us. To study, measure, and reduce its dangers, we have introduced the idea of populations and samples.

The observations which lead to inductive reasoning are regarded as a sample. The inductive reasoning itself is concerned with describing, from the sample, the nature of the population from which the sample was drawn. Right away we see that it is important to know *what* population is being sampled, and that this is closely related to the

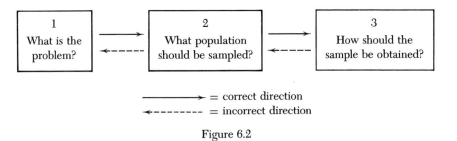

Figure 6.2

question of what problem we are trying to solve. Thus, if we can define our problem, we can define the population from which we sample. Fig. 6.2 shows the situation in diagrammatic form.

Here the solid arrows indicate the proper order of steps. The dotted arrows illustrate a common procedure that should be avoided. If we start with a procedure for obtaining data (3), this determines the population about which we are obtaining information; this in turn decides what problem we are solving, regardless of what we would like to solve. It has been said that data collection is like garbage collection: *before* you collect it you should have in mind what you are going to do with it.

Measurement Error—Problems of Sampling

A basketball court is a poor place to take a sample for estimating the height of the average adult male. Sending a straw ballot to each of a group of corporation presidents, or of union leaders, is a poor way to predict the outcome of a national election. The national attitude on some question cannot be measured well by standing still outside a church, tavern, or college classroom building and asking questions of randomly selected passers-by. Similarly, the average boiling point of water at a particular locality cannot be accurately estimated by taking a series of measurements on a stormy day, when the atmospheric pressure is very low.

All this is to say that populations do not mix themselves homogeneously, whether they are populations of people, vacuum cleaners, missiles, or measurements. In fact, they usually have a strong opposite tendency to segregate into groups that are, within themselves, more homogeneous than the total population. This tendency, unfortunately, has a way of combining with time and space to hamper our efforts to learn by experimentation.

For example, it can be shown that a random sample of 2,500 voters will almost certainly predict the popular vote in a national election to within two percent of the vote. Two important assumptions are implied in this sentence, (a) that a random sample can be obtained, and (b) that the population will not change between the time of sample balloting and the election.

The main obstacle to obtaining a random sample of inhabitants of the United States is their geographical location. To obtain a truly random selection one needs first a list of all the people, and second, enough funds to get in touch with every one selected, no matter how hard he is to find. The next big obstacle is time, for a sample ballot taken today does not contain information about how the electorate may have changed its collective mind by next week.

In less obvious ways, scientific measurements are also subject to this tendency of segregating in time and space. Two similar chemical analyses performed on the same day tend to give much better agreement than will the same procedures carried out several days apart. Similarly, two analyses performed in one laboratory tend to agree better than will two done in different laboratories.

Unfortunately, the procedure of taking a sample is almost always simpler and cheaper if we can work in a limited time interval or in a limited space, or both. Yet what has been said above implies that a sample taken over a certain time period (or in a certain locality) may be good only for that time (or for that locality).

Some scientists, intimidated by this prospect, observe that it was pointed out to them by statisticians, and resolve to have nothing further to do with statistics or the idea of sampling. This action is akin to that of some savage (and some not-so-savage) tribes, who customarily execute the bearers of bad tidings. Whether we like the news or not, a set of measurements is usually taken in order to predict what will occur when future measurements are made. If no measurement is

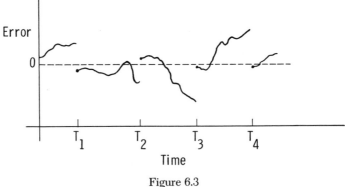

Figure 6.3

repeated, we have no idea how good our prediction is likely to be. If measurements are repeated too closely together, we are apt to overestimate the validity of our prediction.

A simple illustration of these ideas is provided by the drift of instruments. Figure 6.3 shows how this may take place in time. Here the dotted line indicates what the reading on the instrument should be, while the curves show how the instrument reading changes with time. The sudden breaks at times T_1, T_2, T_3, and T_4 are due to calibrations. A calibration is an adjustment of the instrument, by comparison with some known standard. This is an inexact process, which is why the observations made immediately after calibration are not on the dotted line. The dotted line, of course, exists only conceptually, and we never know precisely where it is; if we did, there would be no problem of measurement.

Readings made very close together in time will appear to be quite consistent. (See Fig. 6.4.) For example, readings numbered 1, 2, 3, 4, 5 are very nearly the same. However, they contain a common error, indicated by the arrow. An error which is common to a group of readings is often called a *systematic error,* or *bias,* as opposed to a *random error,* which affects different readings independently. If the five measurements in Fig. 6.4 should be spread out in time, they would take on some of the properties of measurements with random errors; these errors will tend to "average out," that is, the average of several will tend to be more nearly zero than are the individual errors. Systematic error, as illustrated here, is often caused by taking observations too close together in time or space.

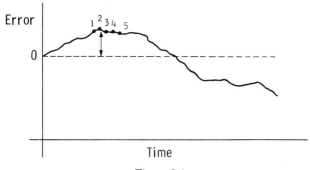

Figure 6.4

The natural tendency of observations, materials, and so on, to come in batches leads to two simple principles of experimentation:

A. In making an absolute measurement, repeated measurements should be spread out over time and space.

B. In making comparative measurements, comparisons should be made as nearly together as possible.

An absolute measurement is one which is intended to answer a question of the type, "How large is X?" A comparative measurement is one which attempts to answer a question such as, "How much larger is X than Y?"

If we take a number of observations too close together (as in Fig. 6.4) then, first, the consistency of our results will mislead us into thinking that our over-all error is much less than it is, and, second, the average of five observations, for example, is scarcely better than a single one. On the other hand, if we follow rule A, we will spread the observations out. This will give instrument drifts (and other relatively slowly changing contributors to error) a chance to make themselves known, and to tend to average out.

Suppose, on the other hand, we have a comparative experiment, perhaps one using the "zero method" mentioned in Chapter Three, "The Methods of Science." For example, two thermoelectric pellets have received different coatings C_1 and C_2 and we wish to compare the resistivities of the two. These should be measured as close together as possible. Any error in the instrument which can be held nearly the same in measuring C_1 and C_2 will have no effect on the comparison. Thus, we are led to principle B, stated above. (Note: It is particularly important not to measure C_1 and C_2 on opposite sides, in time, of a calibration. The calibration change would appear as a difference between C_1 and C_2.)

Any experiment that results in a collection of data is likely to be a complex of absolute and comparative measurements and therefore will demand the use of both principles. The plan for an experiment to use these principles for the efficient collection of data for the stated objective is called the *design* of the experiment. The theory of design of experiments has grown up in the last generation and there are now many books available on the subject. We will mention only some simple examples of how it works.

Example 1. Two objects U and V are given, and we are asked, "What does each weigh?" This leads to absolute measurements, and we weigh each one several times. We shall be disappointed if the person who asked the question uses the answers only to decide which is the heavier. If that was what he wanted to know, he should have said so, for this would have led to comparative measurement. Principle B would have suggested using a pan balance with U in one pan and V in the other, so that the comparison could be made more directly; again, we might do the job several times perhaps, alternating the pans assigned to U and V, but in any case the same total effort would do much more toward correctly comparing the weights of U and V than would the method of absolute measurement.

Example 2. We have a standard scale S_1 and a scale S_2 that we wish to test. This is a comparison. Therefore, when we weigh an object on S_1, we obviously wish to weigh the same object on S_2. No one would fail to use principle B in this fashion. However, it is also prudent to do these weighings close together in time; the "same" object will change slightly with time; for instance in absorbing or losing moisture. The comparison of S_1 and S_2 should include also the use of other objects of different weights, for the comparison of S_1 and S_2 may not be the same at different weights.

Example 3. Some measurements destroy the object measured. Therefore, the comparison of two instruments S_1 and S_2 as in the preceding example, is not possible on the same object. The problem is not insurmountable, however. We can take two objects as nearly alike as possible, and measure one on S_1 and the other on S_2. No conclusion can result from one comparison, but if we make a number of comparisons, the difference between S_1 and S_2 will begin to emerge from the background of differences among the objects measured. Again, the comparisons should be made close together in time.

Example 4. There is a great difference between measuring an object for its own sake and measuring an object to gain information about a class. In the 1961 baseball season, an unusually large number of home runs led to a discussion about possible changes in the nature of the baseball. A 1927 baseball was found and compared "scientifically," according to newspaper accounts, with a 1961 baseball. The balls were found, among other things, to differ in weight by one quarter ounce.

Many people noted the fact that properties of a 1927 baseball were apt to change between 1927 and 1961; few noted that this investigation should have been concerned not merely with measurements on two balls, but on two classes (1927 and 1961) of balls, and that it is therefore impossible to obtain useful information from two balls unless knowledge of variation is available from some other source. A quarter-ounce difference is of no interest to the problem at hand unless other balls have been measured to show that there is much less difference than this among the balls made in the same year.

Example 5. It was implied in the second example that we were testing scale S_2 for "accuracy," that is, to see whether it had any systematic tendency to weigh heavy or light (in comparison to the standard S_1). We are also interested in its "precision," its ability to agree with itself. For this purpose, we weigh the same object several times not too close together. Over this period of time, the same object may have to be checked somehow to see that it has not changed too much in the characteristic being measured. Yet if all measurements are taken too close together, a false apparent precision will be introduced. (Compare Fig. 6.4.)

Example 6. A useful kind of experiment, whose possibilities are often overlooked, is one devoted to estimating the relative importance of different sources of error. If we are to reduce error to the point where it does not seriously interfere with our scientific objectives, we must find those sources which make the largest contribution to the error. Suppose, for example, we have an object that can be measured repeatedly, and we have three instruments (*A*, *B*, and *C*) for making the measurements. Someone has to use the instruments, so we might bring in three observers in order to study the differences that human beings introduce. Finally, we wish to observe the effect of changes in uncontrolled circumstances, and so we might perform our measure-

		Observer		
		I	II	III
	1	C	A	B
Day	2	A	B	C
	3	B	C	A

Figure 6.5

ments on three different days. A possible design for an experiment is shown in Fig. 6.5.

This diagram schedules the experiment as follows: On the first day, 3 measurements are made. These measurements are made by observer I using instrument *C*, observer II using instrument *A*, and observer III using instrument *B*. Procedures for the second and third days are similarly read. This diagram is called a *latin square* and has the property that there is in each row and in each column an *A*, a *B*, and a *C*. The desirability of this kind of symmetry, or balance, is best seen by considering cases in which it does not exist. Consider, for example, the two experiments in Fig. 6.6:

	Observer					Observer		
	I	II	III		I	II	III
1	A	A	A	1	A	B	C
Day 2	B	B	B	2	A	B	C
3	C	C	C	3	A	B	C

Figure 6.6

In the first of these, instrument *A* makes every measurement on the first day, and so on. Thus, if there is any difference among the instruments, for example, instrument *A* tending to read higher than *B* or *C*, this difference will be indistinguishable from any differences among days. Similarly, in the second experiment outlined in Fig. 6.6, any differences among instruments are indistinguishable from differences among observers.

In the experiment of Fig. 6.5, however, the observer effects, the instrument effects, and the daily effects are all separated so that we can recognize them. Suppose, for example, that the experiment is carried out and produces a set of numbers as in Fig. 6.6a:

	Observer		
	I	II	III
1	C(90)	A(88)	B(94)
Day 2	A(96)	B(101)	C(105)
3	B(106)	C(114)	A(106)

Figure 6.6a

57

From this table we obtain the following averages, correct to the nearest integer:

Instrument A:	97	Observer I:	97	Day 1:	91
B:	100	II:	101	2:	101
C:	103	III:	102	3:	109

Some statistical analysis is necessary to help decide whether the observed differences are to be attributed to chance. One thing, however, stands out as a result of the way the experiment was balanced. The observed differences among instruments and among observers are small and may represent random perturbations, but the observed differences among days are considerably larger. If the latter are deemed to be too large to result from experimental error, we can explain them only through something that changes with time. This something may affect the measurements by affecting the instruments, the observers, or the things measured. If we can determine, through further experimentation, the source of this variation, we shall be on the way to its elimination and to a considerable improvement in the precision of our measurement.

Some Figures

7

ALTHOUGH the obvious problems of measurement stem from difficulties of dealing with physical things, there are also problems of pure mathematics involved. The pure mathematician, at least when he is behaving in that capacity, does not measure ordinary objects, but he is sometimes interested in the measurement of geometrical entities. We will therefore digress a bit here to consider some of the purely mathematical problems that arise. This digression will be brief and superficial, not intended to provide depth of understanding, but only to illustrate, by examples involving some ideas of measurement, how mathematicians sometimes develop sophisticated concepts by generalizing very simple ones.

Consider first the process of counting, which is basic to the idea of measurement. One of the earliest problems associated with counting was that of assigning names, both spoken and written, to the positive integers. At first this was done in an arbitrary way, but eventually it was realized that a system was necessary if large numbers were to be easily handled. Makeshift systems, such as that of the Romans, were used until the Arabic system showed its superiority and came to be used in most places where arithmetic has progressed very far. The job of a system, of course, is to provide for the fact that the integers are infinite in number, yet the system, with a finite number of sounds or symbols available, must be able to provide names for numbers as large as people may wish to use.

Once the Arabic decimal system of notation was invented, it might have been supposed that counting was now a dead issue, presenting no new problems. Centuries later, however, new problems did come up when mathematicians began to delve into the meaning of the counting process. Observing that the act of counting the 100 pebbles in a bag, for example, is basically the act of setting up a one-to-one correspondence between the set of pebbles and a standard set (the set of integers from 1 to 100), they considered the application of this idea to infinite sets.

A one-to-one correspondence between the elements of two sets is a relation which associates with each element of either set, one, and only one, element of the other. For example, the set of Arabic integers from 1 to 5 is in one-to-one correspondence with the Roman numerals I to V in this diagram:

$$
\begin{array}{ccccc}
1 & 2 & 3 & 4 & 5 \\
\updownarrow & \updownarrow & \updownarrow & \updownarrow & \updownarrow \\
I & II & III & IV & V
\end{array}
$$

There is nothing surprising about this, of course. However, infinite sets do bring surprises, as illustrated by the following diagram which easily shows the one-to-one correspondence between the set of all positive integers and the set of even positive integers:

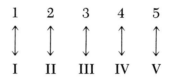

$$
\begin{array}{cccccc}
1 & 2 & 3 & 4 & 5 & \ldots\ldots \\
\updownarrow & \updownarrow & \updownarrow & \updownarrow & \updownarrow & \\
2 & 4 & 6 & 8 & 10 & \ldots\ldots
\end{array}
$$

To each positive integer corresponds one, and only one, even integer, and vice versa. In fact, any infinite set can be placed in one-to-one correspondence with some proper subsets of itself. (A proper subset is a set that is smaller than the whole set and contained in it.) Faced with such a fact, lesser men decided that there is no profit in studying one-to-one correspondences among infinite sets. Others, however, were led to ask whether it is possible to find infinite sets which cannot be placed in one-to-one correspondence with each other. Some were found, and the theory of transfinite numbers was on its way, aided primarily by G. Cantor (1845–1918).

Any infinite set which can be put in one-to-one correspondence with the positive integers is called "countable." The word is also applied to all finite sets, for obvious reasons. The rational numbers, which include not only the positive and negative integers and 0, but also all quotients of integers (except those with 0 denominators) are countable, too. To show this, we display the positive rational numbers in the following diagram, the rule of formation of which is obvious:

$$\frac{1}{1} \quad \frac{2}{1} \quad \frac{3}{1} \quad \frac{4}{1} \quad \cdots \cdots$$

$$\frac{1}{2} \quad \frac{2}{2} \quad \frac{3}{2} \quad \frac{4}{2} \quad \cdots \cdots$$

$$\frac{1}{3} \quad \frac{2}{3} \quad \frac{3}{3} \quad \frac{4}{3} \quad \cdots \cdots$$

$$\frac{1}{4} \quad \frac{2}{4} \quad \frac{3}{4} \quad \frac{4}{4} \quad \cdots \cdots$$

$$\cdot \qquad \cdot \qquad \cdot \qquad \cdot$$
$$\cdot \qquad \cdot \qquad \cdot \qquad \cdot$$
$$\cdot \qquad \cdot \qquad \cdot \qquad \cdot$$

This diagram contains obvious duplications. These may be omitted in counting or, more simply, we may fall back on the fact that a subset of a countable set is countable. Thus we need only show that the numbers in the diagram are countable, which we do by following this path:

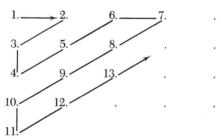

This figure shows how we move through the preceding diagram, counting as we go. Following the designated path, we see that each number in the diagram receives a single positive integer name, and each integer is used once and only once in the process, which is what we mean by a one-to-one correspondence. To include the negative rational numbers, we would have only to set up a similar path through them, and assign even integers to the positive rationals and odd integers to the negative rationals.

A little bit of this might persuade some people that all sets are countable. If this were true, the concept of countability would be of no interest. Consider, however, the set of all real numbers, which includes the rationals, irrationals such as $\sqrt{2}$, $\sqrt{3}$, $\sqrt[4]{5} + \sqrt{3}$ and so on, plus transcendental numbers that cannot be generated algebraically, such as π and e. The problem of defining this set is beyond the mathematics we are using here, but we shall assume familiarity with the infinite decimal representation of numbers, as

$$\frac{5}{11} = 0.45555\ldots.$$

$$\sqrt{2} = 1.41421\ldots.$$

$$\pi = 3.14159\ldots.$$

Now if the real numbers (the collection of these infinite decimals) were countable, this would mean that a rule could be devised for putting them all in a list. That is, the rule would specify names $n_1, n_2, n_3, \ldots$ for the real numbers so that to each would correspond one and only one n_i. To show that this is impossible, we proceed by assuming that it can be done, and show that the assumption leads to a contradiction. The supposition that the numbers between 0 and 1 are countable implies a list like this:

$$n_1 = 0.312456\ldots$$
$$n_2 = 0.427731\ldots$$
$$n_3 = 0.884256\ldots$$
$$n_4 = 0.642039\ldots$$

.

.

.

In order to show that such a list cannot contain all the real numbers between 0 and 1, it is necessary only to show that there is always at least one number that is not in the list. One way to do this is to form a number n whose first digit is anything but 3 (the first digit of n_1), whose second digit is anything but 2 (the second digit of n_2), whose third digit is anything but 4 (the third digit of n_3), and, in general, whose ith digit is anything but the ith digit of n_i. Thus, the new number is not in the list since it differs from every number of the list in at least one digit.

(Note: In a rigorous proof of this result, it is necessary to take into account possible duplication caused by numbers ending in all nines, as 0.19999 . . . , and which are also expressible as numbers ending in all zeros, such as 0.20000 . . .)

We now have two infinite sets which do not have the same cardinal number, that is, their elements cannot be put into one-to-one correspondence. The first is the infinite countable set, of which several examples have been given, and the second is called the *continuum,* or the set of real numbers. The cardinal numbers corresponding to these two sets are usually written $\aleph_o$ (aleph null) and $\aleph_1$ (or c) respectively.

Cantor went on to show that larger and larger classes could be built indefinitely, starting from the continuum, and the cardinal numbers of these classes are called the *transfinite* numbers. There is a conjecture, called the "continuum hypothesis," that there is no cardinal number larger than $\aleph_o$ but smaller than $\aleph_1$, but this has not been proved.

From counting we progress to another simple kind of measurement, namely, finding the length of a simple line segment. Ancient geometers were interested in the problem of "incommensurables," which refers to the fact that it is possible to construct two line segments which cannot both be measured exactly in terms of any common unit. This possibility is easily established as follows:

Take an isosceles right triangle as in Fig. 7.1. If the hypotenuse and either side are commensurable, this means that there is a unit of length such that AB and BC are, respectively, exactly m units and n units long, where m and n are integers. Further, it is possible to choose the unit so that m and n are not both even integers. (For if m and n are both even, then the unit length can be doubled and the sides have new lengths $m/2$ and $n/2$. If these integers are both even, the unit can be

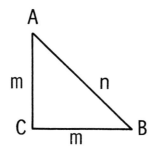

Figure 7.1

doubled again, and this can be repeated until at least one of the two lengths is odd.) Now, by the Pythagorean theorem,

$$m^2 + m^2 = n^2,$$

or $$n^2 = 2m^2.$$

Hence, n^2 is even, being equal to twice an integer, and so n itself is even, since an odd number squared is always odd. Thus we can write $n = 2p$, where p is an integer, and $n^2 = 2m^2$ becomes

$$4p^2 = 2m^2$$

or $$m^2 = 2p^2.$$

The same argument can now be repeated to show that m is also even, so a contradiction has been reached, forcing us to abandon the assumption that AB and BC are commensurable.

Ancient mathematicians were profoundly disturbed by the discovery of incommensurability. They ascribed to it all manner of dire consequences, including the ugly thought that mathematics might not be the beautiful, unified whole that they had thought it to be. Part of this trouble was that the Greeks' infatuation with geometry had led them to neglect arithmetic, and their development of the number system was lagging behind their development of geometry. It turned out that the problem of establishing the existence of numbers to correspond to the lengths of all possible line segments was a difficult one and it was not laid to rest until the latter part of the nineteenth century. The problem was to define the real numbers and to describe the nature of the infinite line in such a way as to set up a one-to-one correspondence between the real numbers and the points on the line. Those interested in pursuing this problem will find it discussed in various places, such as the early chapters of textbooks on the theory of functions of a real variable.

Incommensurable line segments gave rise to a serious problem in the measurement of area. In elementary geometry, all area formulas are based on the fact that the area of a rectangle $ABCD$ (Fig. 7.2) is equal to the product of the sides, or $AB \times BC$. This is shown intuitively by dividing the rectangle into square units, m along BC and n along AB, from which it obviously follows that there are exactly mn such units contained in $ABCD$. If AB and BC are incommensurable, though,

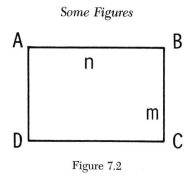

Figure 7.2

this easy explanation becomes unavailable, and the area of a rectangle must be defined in terms of limits of areas involving various units.

Once the idea of limits is included, it would appear that one kind of area is as simple as another. We could define the area of an irregular figure, such as shown in Fig. 7.3, for example, by first considering the two possibilities illustrated. On the left, for a given grid, is shown (shaded) the set of squares which are all entirely contained in the area. On the right is shown (shaded) the set of squares which are required to cover the area entirely. Let $\underline{A}$ be the area of the shaded group on the left, $\overline{A}$ that of the group on the right, and A the area of the curved region. Obviously we wish to define A so that it will always be true that

$$\underline{A} \leq A \leq \overline{A}.$$

We think of all possible grids and therefore all possible $\underline{A}$ and $\overline{A}$, and we are interested in

$$L = \text{least upper bound of } \underline{A}$$

and $\qquad G = \text{greatest lower bound of } \overline{A}.$

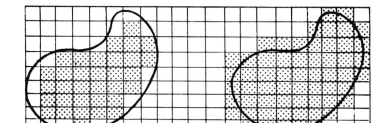

Figure 7.3

That is, L is the smallest number not exceeded by any $\underline{A}$, while G is the largest number that does not exceed any $\overline{A}$. It may be "intuitively obvious" that $G = L$, but the difficulty in proving this follows from the fact that it is not necessarily true. In the ordinary case where $G = L$, the common value of these two quantities is naturally defined as A. The discovery of regions, more complicated, of course, than that shown in the figure, for which L is actually less than G, helped to lead to the development of modern measure theory.

To illustrate the kind of complexity that can occur in what would appear to be simple measurement problems, we do not have to go beyond the problem of measuring on a straight line. On an infinite straight line (Fig. 7.4) let us select a point 0 to be the origin, lay down an arbitrarily chosen unit distance to the right and call the resulting point 1. Then in terms of this unit, we can, as mentioned earlier, associate with each point a unique real number which may be called its abscissa.

On such a line, the length of a line segment AB is given by $B - A$, if A and B may also represent the abscissas of the points that they identify. If CD is another line segment, not overlapping, it is clearly desirable to be able to think of AB and CD together and to speak of their "total length," which we naturally expect to be $(B - A) + (D - C)$. As soon as we speak of the collective length of two or more line segments, it is natural to go on to infinite collections. For example, we might have a set of intervals of lengths ½, ¼, ⅛, ¹⁄₁₆, ..., and anyone who has studied infinite geometric progressions knows that the sum of these numbers is 1, and so it makes sense to speak of this as the *measure*, a term which we shall now use in place of length, of the whole collection. Those who have not studied infinite geometrical progressions can verify this particular result by the following geometric interpretation: Take a line segment 1 unit long (Fig. 7.4a) and mark off at the left a distance equal to ½ unit, as shown. Then take half the remaining distance, which is ¼, then half the remaining distance again,

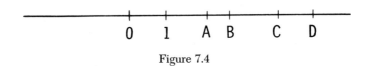

Figure 7.4

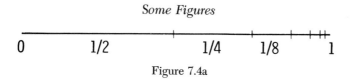

Figure 7.4a

which is ⅛, and so on. Obviously these segments will never pass the point 1, and yet we can come as close to 1 as we like, provided we take enough of the segments. This is what we mean when we say that the sum of the whole collection of lengths is 1.

When infinite collections are allowed, we eventually arrive at the idea of measuring arbitrary collections of points. For example, on the line of Fig. 7.4a, the points between 0 and 1 can be divided into two sets, those with rational abscissas and those with irrational abscissas. Can we measure these sets? Suppose we look first at the rational points. Since they are countable, we can make a list of them,

$$P_1, P_2, P_3, \ldots$$

Now suppose that we cover P_1 with a segment of length $\epsilon/2$, P_2 with a segment of length $\epsilon/4$, P_3 with one of length $\epsilon/8$, and so on through the list. These segments will have a collective content that cannot be exceeded by that of the collection of P's, no matter how small ϵ is. But this collective content is

$$\frac{\epsilon}{2} + \frac{\epsilon}{4} + \frac{\epsilon}{8} + \cdots$$
$$= \epsilon \left(\frac{1}{2} + \frac{1}{4} + \frac{1}{8} + \cdots \right)$$
$$= \epsilon,$$

since we have already seen that the sum of the indicated series is 1. Now if the content of the collection of P's is less than or equal to ϵ no matter how small ϵ is, then the content must be zero. Therefore, if we are allowed to subtract, the content of the collection of irrational points must be 1, that is, the entire content of the original segment. Speaking in intuitive terms, then, we may say that the points in a line are so numerous that the removal of a countably infinite number has no effect on the content as we have defined it.

Modern measure theory is used to attack the problem of measuring various point sets in one or more dimensions. At the very outset a major conflict must be settled. We would like to have an additive property, that is, that the measure of the sum of non-overlapping sets be the sum of their measures. Also we would like to have the measure of a single point be zero. Yet every set is a sum of single points, so that these two requirements together would assign zero measure to every set, a result that is hardly calculated to arouse interest. In fact, there is a third requirement, namely, that this generalized measure, when applied to simple point sets such as line segments, interiors of circles or cubes, should agree with the known lengths, areas, or volumes of these well-known sets. The conflict is resolved by limiting the additivity property to finite sums and certain, but not all, infinite sums; this leaves some sets "unmeasurable," but nevertheless permits a theory which is consistent with all classical results and presents many new ones.

In order that measure theory be related to more than just geometric sets, the theory develops from the point of view of point sets with functions defined over them. Thus the measure of a set is defined in terms of a function which may be interpreted as a distribution of "mass" over the set; if only the length, area, or volume of the set is desired, the function is simply taken to be 1 everywhere. To take a simple example, consider a cube of side a (Fig. 7.5) whose density ρ increases from top to bottom, so that $\rho = k(a - z)$, for example, where k is a constant. Then the weight of a horizontal cross-section of thickness dz is approximately

$$a^2 k(a - z)dz,$$

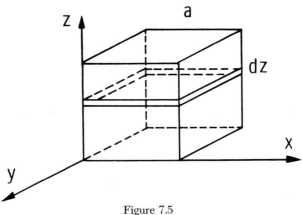

Figure 7.5

and the weight of the cube may be found by adding up such horizontal slices by integration, namely,

$$\int_0^a a^2 k(a - z)dz = a^4 k/2.$$

A physical illustration of this kind of thing may be found in a vertical column of the earth's atmosphere, in which the density increases continuously down the column. The number $a^4 k/2$ can be considered a measure of the cube just as well as the number a^3, which results when we are interested only in the volume.

In these terms we can regard all of integral calculus as a part of measure theory. The reason for this can be illustrated by the fact that any integral

$$\int_a^b f(x)dx$$

can be interpreted as the measure of mass of the line segment from a to b when a mass density function $f(x)$ is applied along the line.

It may come as a surprise to some to learn that the entire theory of probability is also a part of measure theory. In an experiment, the class of possible outcomes is called the *sample space* S. A subset S* of S is called an *event*. If a "mass" can be distributed over S so that the measure of S is 1, then the mass belonging to S* can be interpreted as the probability of the event S*. Purely mathematical treatments of probability now customarily introduce the subject along these lines.

Having observed that probability is a part of measure theory, let us return from these abstractions to the simpler things of life and consider an example in which probability might be used in the theory and practice of measurement. Returning to the problem of incommensurables, we let AB be a line segment and u be a unit line segment, supposing only that AB is between m and $m + 1$ units long, where m is an integer. We proceed to show how AB can be measured with u, whether or not they are commensurable, given a simple idea from probability.

To invest this idea with the proper authority, we state it as follows:

Postulate: Let it be granted that a line segment CD may be dropped on a line segment AB in such a way that (a) the two lines make a straight angle, (b) A lies between C and D, (c) for any subsegment EF of CD,

69

Figure 7.6

the probability that *EF* falls on *A* is *EF/CD*, that is, this probability depends only on the length of *EF*, and not on its position. (See Fig. 7.6.)

The act postulated may be described as dropping *CD* randomly along *AB* at *A*. Suppose now that we drop the unit line *u* (see above) randomly on *AB* at *A*, as illustrated in Fig. 7.7, with $m = 2$:

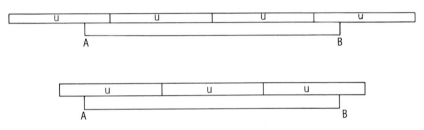

Figure 7.7

Depending on how *u* falls on *A*, it then takes either 3 *u*'s or 4 *u*'s to cover *AB*, and the length of *AB* is "measured" at 2 or 3 units in these two cases respectively. We next compute the probability associated with each of these cases by observing the configuration of Fig. 7.8, where the first *u* is so placed that the third *u* ends exactly at B: If *u'* represents the (unshaded) part of *u* protruding to the left of *A*, we see that the length of *AB* is $3 - u'$. In general, it is clear that whenever the unshaded part of the first unit covers *A*, the segment *AB* will be covered by 3 units and measured as 2; otherwise 4 units are needed to cover *AB* and it is measured as 3. From the above postulate, the probability that the unshaded segment covers A is u'/u, or just u', since *u* is our unit.

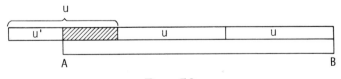

Figure 7.8

Therefore,

> (probability of obtaining measurement 2) $= u'$;
> (probability of obtaining measurement 3) $= 1 - u'$.

Now it can be shown that the average measurement by this process is

$$2(u') + 3(1 - u') = 3 - u',$$

which is just the length of AB, as seen above. Thus our measurement is correct "on the average." Obviously there is no difficulty in expressing these steps in terms of a general m.

Finally, if this measurement process is repeated, say, n times, and the average measurement so obtained is called d, it can be shown that the variance of d is

$$\text{var } d = \frac{u'(1 - u')}{n}.$$

Since u' is fixed, this means that we can make the variance of d as small as we please by making n sufficiently large.

The significance of the last statement can be illustrated by our earlier problem of trying to measure a segment of length $\sqrt{2}$ with a segment of length 1. Here $m = 1$ and u' is $2 - \sqrt{2}$, so that the variance of the result d of averaging n measurements is

$$\text{var } d = \frac{(2 - \sqrt{2})(-1 + \sqrt{2})}{n} = \frac{-4 + 3\sqrt{2}}{n} = \frac{0.2426}{n}$$

and so the standard deviation is about $0.493/\sqrt{n}$. It is known that for n not too small, d is approximately normally distributed. Thus, from the variance, we can compute the probability that d differs from the correct answer by less than a given amount. For example, to come within 0.1 of the correct answer with probability 0.5 requires 12 observations; probabilities 0.9, 0.95, and 0.99 require 66, 94, and 161 observations, respectively. Changing the figure 0.1 to 0.01, say, requires multiplying the number of observations by 100.

In general, for any line segment AB, or any u, and for any given $\epsilon > 0$ and $\rho < 1$, we can find an n such that n observations will, with probability ρ, produce a result with error less than ϵ. In particular, a yardstick marked off only in feet can be used to measure a length to a quarter of an inch, if we put the yardstick down "randomly" a sufficiently large number of times. Thus, though the procedure has little practical significance with respect to the measurement of distances, it illustrates the fact that the ordinary limiting process is not the only way to treat incommensurables. The magic phrase "it can be shown" has been used several times to avoid having to go into too much mathematics for our present purposes. Anyone from Missouri is referred to the subject "binomial distribution" in almost any textbook on probability and statistics.

Extending the Senses

Part
3

Only Human

8

ALL LIVING THINGS, whether plant or animal, are equipped with mechanisms that enable them to react to external stimuli. The sunflower is only one of many plants that turn with the sun, so that the face of the flower will intercept the sun's rays. A cricket's chirping is governed by the temperature of its surroundings. Wild animals stalk their prey, aided by their special ability to detect sounds and odors. Butterflies, hundreds of yards apart, are able to locate each other through a sense of smell. Bats, gliding on silent wings, use an ultrasonic sonar system to avoid obstacles and intercept insects. In each case, survival depends on the reception and interpretation of information concerning environment.

In a more sophisticated way, man too depends on his sense of perception. A newborn baby, for example, senses a strange environment, and immediately reacts by voicing displeasure. As the baby develops physically, he learns to interpret information about the outside world. Certain events follow a set pattern, and therefore predictions can be made, based on observations or sensing experiences. Wood placed in a fire will burn; rocks will not. It is easier to see in the dark after having been there for some time. A flash of lightning is followed by a clap of thunder; a basket of rocks is harder to lift than a basket of leaves. All such information becomes a part of a vast store of knowledge from which man can formulate laws of nature to describe the behavior of his surroundings.

We are continually measuring our environment, either consciously or unconsciously. Sometimes this is done for us automatically. For example, we perspire on a hot humid day because our body temperature regulator is measuring changes in the environmental temperature and humidity, and attempting to compensate for these changes. When we look at a bright light, the pupils of our eyes close to keep the light intensity on the retina below a given level. Our environment is continually changing, and our sensing mechanisms are continually reacting to the changes.

We can measure only what we perceive through our senses. The number of human senses varies from five to eleven, depending on the definition. All lists contain five basic senses: sight, hearing, touch, taste and smell; some also include senses of heat, gravity, posture (muscle sense), hunger, thirst and pain. Those dealing mostly with the internal being are not pertinent to our present discussion. Of particular interest, however, are the basic senses that allow man to make contact with the outside world and gain information about his surroundings. Located in the body, highly specialized cells called receptors receive this information. These receptors function by transforming various kinds of energy into electrical energy, which in turn stimulates certain brain centers. Devices that transform energy from one form to another are called *transducers*. Our senses of touch and hearing rely on changes in pressure on certain receptor cells. This type of transducer is *mechanical-electrical* or *electromechanical*. The senses of taste and smell depend on chemical reactions; these are *electrochemical* in nature. The sense of sight is dependent on *photochemical, photoelectric,* and *electrochemical* actions combined in a manner not yet clearly understood.

It is obvious that a measurement cannot be made unless some physical effect is first detected or sensed. Detection is not to be confused with measurement; it is only qualitative in nature, whereas measurement is quantitative, which implies comparing the result with a standard. For example, we can observe a light and describe it as "bright" or "dim," or "reddish in color," but these terms convey very little useful information. It is bright compared to *what,* and how much is "bright"? Not until we describe the light in terms of the energy per unit area, or its spectral characteristics in wavelengths, which implies comparisons to standards, is the information meaningful for most scientific purposes.

Even when we are asleep, we continue to receive information from our environment, although at a decreased level. This is illustrated by our being awakened by an alarm clock or a thunderstorm. We react to such information and make judgments. Primitive man, and even our ancestors of only a few hundred years ago, relied almost solely on the five natural senses as the primary means of gaining information. Highly sensitive and entirely adequate for many purposes, our receptors are unreliable, however, for a complete understanding of our environment. For example, although the human eye is extremely sensitive to visible electromagnetic radiation—light—it cannot detect ultraviolet rays. Anyone who has suffered a severe burn from overexposure to the sun is familiar with the painful consequences of this particular human inability. Since our eyes are able to detect only a very narrow range of electromagnetic radiation, a variety of sensors and detectors have been developed to supplement our sense of sight, extending detection to both longer and shorter wavelengths. Such devices enable us to measure the size and determine the weight of molecules we cannot possibly see with the naked eye.

Sensing is accomplished through a number of observables. The sense of sight allows us to observe physical dimensions, change of position or shape, the color and intensity of light—electromagnetic radiation. With our sense of hearing we detect intensity, quality, and pitch of sound—changes in pressure of sound waves. Through our sense of touch and muscle sense we observe pressures and forces, and derive a sense of equilibrium and gravity. From our awareness of gravity, we observe weight, or the more fundamental quantity, mass. Through our senses of taste and smell, we detect the presence of chemicals or foreign molecules in the air or in the water we drink. From these and other observables, such as the passage of time, changes in temperature, and the velocity of moving objects, we are able to form judgments about our environment. Making measurements of these observable phenomena enables scientists to formulate theories and laws to explain the behavior of nature.

Because physics is a science of measurement and sensing is a prerequisite to measurement, new scientific discoveries depend largely on man's ingenuity in developing new sensors or inventing new combinations of existing devices. As we discuss some of the more modern sensing techniques in terms of extensions of man's natural senses, we will become aware that in the final analysis man is still confronted with certain limitations; in scientific investigation this is a major challenge.

Sensing Pressure and Sound

9

THE SENSE of hearing, or detection of sound, is one of the most important means of receiving information. In the early days of history, man relied on the detection of sound to sense danger or the presence of game for food. For thousands of years, hearing played a major role in man's struggle for survival, and even today it is a primary means of communication, important to our understanding and interpretation of our surroundings.

The definition of sound depends on the point of view adopted. The old controversy about whether or not a falling tree makes a sound when no one is in the forest to hear it can be debated forever, unless terms are defined and a distinction is made between what occurs external to the human body and what occurs within the ear. Subjectively, sound may be regarded as the sense impressions of the organ of hearing. Objectively, it may be considered the vibrating motion that produces this sensation.

Sound waves are produced by the mechanical vibration of an object. If the vibration is regular, we may call it music; if it is irregular, we are apt to call it noise. For example, the regular vibrations of a violin string produce a musical note, but a door slamming or a machine vibrating produces a noise. Sound waves are longitudinal; the particles transmitting the sound travel back and forth in the direction of wave propagation. In this respect, they may be regarded as pressure waves, as illustrated by the tuning fork in Fig. 9.1. As a prong advances it compacts the air molecules before it, making for more molecules per unit of volume. Alternately, the opposite side of the prong is moving away from the molecules, rarefying them, or producing fewer molecules per unit of volume. Pressure is given by

$$p = nkT,$$

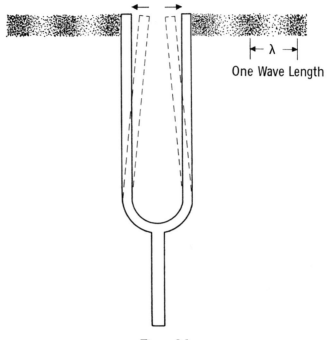

One Wave Length

Figure 9.1

where n is the number of molecules per unit volume, k is the Boltzmann constant, and T is the temperature. We can see from this equation that sound waves in air are regularly spaced changes in air pressure. As the prong vibrates faster, the compressed regions are closer together. If we could count the number of air molecules per unit volume as a function of distance from the vibrating source, we would observe a periodic change in density, given by the same type of law as that governing wave motion. Hence, the term *sound waves*. The distance between two adjacent points of maximum density is a *wavelength*. Air waves strike the eardrum and set it in motion; through a series of bones, the vibrations are transmitted to the inner ear, where they are sensed as sound by the auditory nerve. It is not yet fully understood just how vibratory motions in the inner ear are converted into a sense of hearing. However, we do know that the mechanism is one in which a mechanical motion is converted into electrical energy.

The ear can distinguish three characteristics of sound: loudness, pitch, and quality. Loudness is related to intensity, but it is not the same. Intensity is the energy of the sound waves; loudness is the strength of the sensation registered by the eardrum. Different people, receiving exactly the same intensity of sound, may experience quite different sensations of loudness. For this reason, the only objective way to measure magnitude of sound is to determine the intensity or energy; the measuring unit is usually given in terms of dynes/cm^2, or sometimes in pressure per unit time.

The ear can respond to a very large range of sound intensity. In many applications, it is the *change* in this intensity which is important. For such measurements, the ratio of sound intensities is given in *decibels* (db). The ratio of the loudest sound we can hear without pain, to the power of the weakest sound we are just able to detect, is about 1,000,000,000,000 to 1. This is not a very convenient way to write such a large number, so we express it as a power of ten, which gives the ratio $10^{12} : 1$. Using logarithms, we then have

$$\log_{10} 10^{12} = 12.$$

We use the term *bel* to mean the exponent that represents the power ratio. For example, $10^{12} : 1$ becomes simply 12 bels. A decibel is one-tenth of a bel, and so the power ratio to which the ear can respond is a range of 120 decibels, or 120 db. Thus, the decibel I can be written:

$$I = 10 \log_{10} \frac{p_1}{p_2}.$$

A power ratio of 20 db is equal to the ratio of 100:1.

At the threshold of hearing, the normal ear can detect a change of about one decibel—the barest audible whisper. The rustle of leaves in a slight breeze has a loudness of 10 db, and the normal speaking voice has about 60 db. At approximately 140 db, the average person experiences pain.

The minimum amount of power the ear can detect at 1000 cycles per second is 10^{-16} watts/cm^2. In terms of intensity, the sound waves at the threshold of hearing correspond to a pressure change of 10^{-9} atmospheres, approximately 10^{-6} mm Hg (mercury). This is about 100 times more sensitive than the most sensitive diaphragm manometer used in the laboratory to measure changes in pressure. The change in pressure due to change in altitude is about 1 mm Hg for 11 meters of height. Aircraft use altimeters that can detect changes of a few feet, corresponding to pressure changes of about 0.1 mm Hg. Pressure changes of 10^{-9} atmospheres (the threshold of hearing) striking the eardrum will move it through an amplitude of less than 10^{-8} cm, a distance less than the diameter of a hydrogen atom. This is remarkable, since the eardrum and the inner ear are connected only by a series of bone joints. It seems truly wonderful that such extremely small movements can be transmitted by these mechanical couplings.

As to the pitch, or frequency of sound vibration, the human ear can detect frequencies from about 20 cy/sec to as high as 20,000 cy/sec. With increasing age, our ability to hear high frequencies decreases sharply, particularly when it comes to distinguishing variations of pitch at high frequencies. Intense sound at high frequencies is actually felt rather than heard. When two notes are sounded alternately in the most sensitive range (500 to 4,000 cy/sec), the ear can detect a difference in frequency of about 1 cycle in every 300 cy/sec. However, if the two notes are sounded simultaneously, the ear is able to detect a difference in frequency, or beats, corresponding to 1 cycle in 20,000 cy/sec.

Although the human ear is incapable of discerning sound with frequencies greater than about 20,000 cy/sec, much higher frequencies do exist, and many animals are able to detect them. Dogs, for example, can hear much higher frequencies, and we have already mentioned that bats navigate at night by means of an ultrasonic sonar system. Frequencies above the audible have been termed *ultrasonics,* which until recently went up to about 500 megacycles (500 $\times$ 10^6 cy/sec). New techniques have now extended this frequency range to 10 kilo-megacycles (1×10^{10} cy/sec); the term *hypersonics* designates this range.

Ultrasonic waves, projected against a boundary, produce two effects: alternating pressure at the frequency of wave propagation, and direct pressure due to the radiation. The generation of ultrasonic waves is the inverse of their detection. They are generated by the mechanical vibrations of a crystal placed in a rapidly alternating electric field. This mechanical motion creates sound or pressure waves; these are intercepted by a second crystal, which vibrates in turn, its mechanical motion producing an electric current that is amplified and measured. The crystalline materials used possess such a quality that when they are squeezed or bent or twisted, an electric field is developed across the crystal structure. This *piezoelectric* effect is used by many phonograph pickups; the phonograph needle, riding in the record groove, vibrates a crystal, producing an electrical signal which is fed into an amplifier.

Just as in any mechanical vibrating motion, resonances can occur at definite frequencies, called the *resonant* or *natural* frequencies. If an elastic body is vibrated at its natural frequency, it is possible to build up large amplitudes of vibration, depending on the forces applied and on the frictional or damping forces in the vibrating system. Therefore, crystals can be cut with a certain thickness and in a particular way to give large amplitudes at specific frequencies; crystals of this kind are used in crystal oscillators. This same characteristic may also be used in the detecting crystal where we are interested in the intensity changes of specific frequency.

A modification of these ultrasonic techniques is used to study magnetic effects on crystals. For example, if a crystal is set into vibration at a certain frequency in a magnetic field strong enough to influence the magnetic moments of the crystal atoms, it is possible to control the vibrations of the crystal by the magnetic effects. This changes the frequency of vibration and, if at resonance, may produce a large change in amplitude. By combining ultrasonics with magnetic resonances, scientists are able to study the physical properties of crystals. This is becoming a powerful tool in the study of magnetism.

Certain ferromagnetic materials, called *ferrites*, have the property of changing physical dimensions when placed in a magnetic field. This *magnetostriction* is used to generate powerful ultrasonic waves, and in some instances it is also used in detectors.

The detection of sound frequently requires using two or more sensors to translate the information into a form that the human senses can discern. There is an optical method for detecting ultrasonic waves, for example, which couples the ultrasonic generator to a liquid in a small tank. If the waves move through the liquid and are reflected at the far end of the tank in the proper phase, *standing waves* are produced. This means there are regions where the liquid is alternately under compression and expansion. Light waves of a specific wavelength, traveling with a velocity that depends on the density of the medium, are passed through the liquid. It is a familiar fact that if an object is partially submerged, the portion below the surface level of the liquid appears to be in the wrong place. For example, if a stick projects above the level of a liquid, it appears bent. This is because liquid has an *index of refraction* different from that of air. In the ultrasonic tank, the indices of refraction will be different in the compressed portions and the expanded portions. This regular spacing of liquid with different indices of refraction produces a kind of grating. When light passes through this dynamic diffraction grating, it forms a series of interference bands, which can be photographed or measured with a photocell.

Receptor cells of another class, sensitive to pressure, are located on the surface of the human body. Others, dispersed throughout our muscles, give rise to sensations of body movement, or muscle sense. Even with our eyes shut we can still tell the relative positions of our arms and legs. For example, with closed eyes it is possible to extend the arms, bend and rotate them in a series of involved movements, and then without hesitation bring the tips of the index fingers together. This is because the cells that are activated by movements of our muscles respond commensurately to changes as the muscles are flexed. From these receptors we also derive, at least partially, a sense of weight, or the action of gravity.

Ever since man first tried to pick up a stone or a log, he has realized that all objects resist his efforts to lift them. Primitive man found that rocks could be lifted easily if they were small, but that large rocks were more difficult to move. He observed that lifting a log required less effort than raising a rock of comparable size. If he chanced to live near a volcano, he probably discovered that volcanic rocks were easy to lift, even though they were much larger than others. He must have wondered why all weights were more difficult to manage as he grew older. Without doubt, man was first concerned with weight because this determined how much he could lift.

Any discussion of weight begins with the more fundamental unit, *mass*. Mass is defined as the amount of matter in a physical body. Quantitatively, it can only be measured in terms of forces acting on a body. Mass is that property which gives a body *inertia;* that is, resistance to being moved, accelerated, or decelerated. Thus, mass may be defined by the equation:

$$\text{Force} = \text{mass} \times \text{acceleration}.$$

If a body with a certain quantity of matter (mass) were hung from a spring, and the equilibrium position were designated by a sensitive pointer, this pointer would change as the spring was moved from the equator to the North Pole. The intrinsic quantity of matter—its mass—has not changed; what has changed is its pull on the spring. This pull is called its *weight*, and the weight changed because it is defined by the force of gravity, which varies at different distances from the center of the earth. Since the earth is not perfectly spherical, the force of gravity is greater at the poles than at the equator.

With muscles stretched over the bones of his skeleton acting as levers, an average man can lift a weight of one to two hundred pounds (about 10^5 grams) against the earth's gravity. On the moon, the same man would be able to lift six times as much, since the force of gravity is proportionately less.

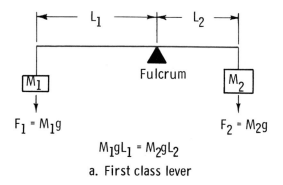

a. First class lever

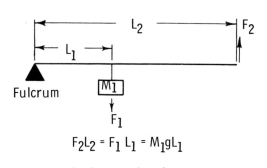

b. Second class lever

Figure 9.2

When we weigh an object, we are actually measuring a comparison between the gravitational pull on the object and a like pull on a standard weight or standard object. By ingenious use of the law of the lever, scientists and engineers have devised a series of scales or balances capable of a very wide range of measurement. The law of the lever, illustrated in Fig. 9.2, states that in equilibrium or balance, the forces around the pivot, or fulcrum, must be equal. Thus,

$$F_1L_1 = F_2L_2 = M_1gL_1 = M_2gL_2,$$

where M is the mass, g is the acceleration of gravity, and L is the distance from the pivot to the point through which the force F is directed. Since g remains constant for any particular weighing, we are able to directly compare two different masses. By moving the pivot very close to one end, a very heavy weight can be compared with a much lighter one. Part b of Fig. 9.2 shows a variation of the balance, utilizing a second-class lever. Note that in the first-class lever the pivot is always between the two forces, which act in the same direction; the pivot of the second-class lever, however, is at one end, and the forces are opposite in direction. This type of balance is used for weighing very heavy objects. Fig. 9.3 shows how the principle is applied to the *beam balance*, such as that used in a doctor's office. The platform is supported at pivot A, and the other end of this second-class lever is supported at pivot B by the vertical rod, which is hinged at point C. This is one end of the first-class lever pivoted at D and balanced by the weight M.

Balances that work on this principle are used to weigh loaded freight cars, where the total weight is about 25,000 pounds, or 10^7 grams. In contrast, a modern chemical balance is delicate enough to weigh the ink used to print one letter on this page. Based on the first-class lever, this type of balance must be enclosed in a box so that air currents will not disturb the weighing process. With such highly refined balances, it is possible to weigh minute masses of only 10^{-7} grams.

The quartz balance is a special adaptation, shown in Fig. 9.4. This balance is constructed from thin quartz fibers only a fraction of a millimeter in diameter, which are fused with a hot flame to form a light, strong frame. Fine tungsten wires, sealed into the frame, act as pivots. Usually the balance is enclosed in a container which can be evacuated. When such balances are used by physical chemists to study surface

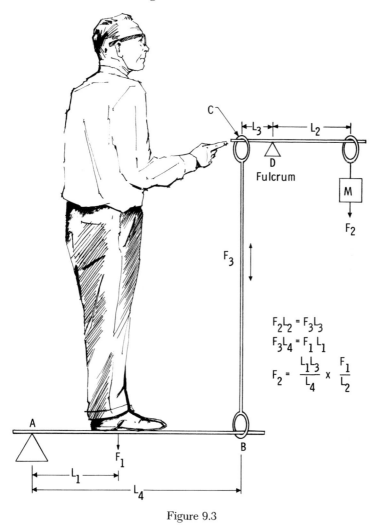

Figure 9.3

reactions, a small sample of metal is fastened to one of the arms; the other arm contains a piece of magnetic material that moves in a magnetic field. The force exerted by the magnetic field is used to balance the gravitational force of the material under study. If a small amount of oxygen is admitted to the system and the metal is heated by an external furnace, oxidation will take place at the surface of the metal. The balance is so sensitive that it can detect an increase in weight due to a single layer of oxygen atoms on the metal surface. If the change

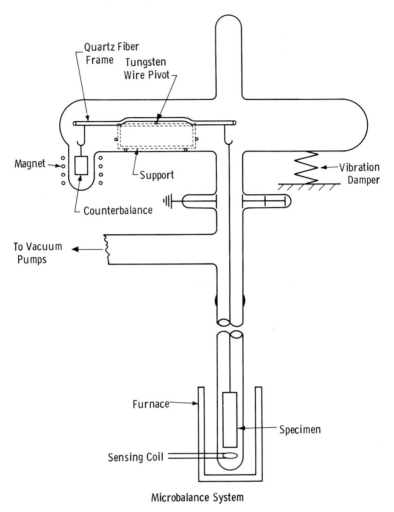

Microbalance System

Figure 9.4

in weight is measured as a function of time, the oxidation rate can be determined.

Some of the most sensitive pressure receptors in the human body are associated with our sense of touch. Of course, the sensitivity varies in different areas of the skin. On the forehead or the back of the forearm, for example, a weight of .002 grams can be felt pressing on a area of 9 square millimeters. Smaller weights can be detected if the weight touches a fine hair, such as an eyelash. This is because the eyelash acts as a lever, exerting pressure on the receptor cell at the base of the hair, and producing an electrical current through this electromechanical transducer.

Atomic scientists, who need to determine exceedingly small masses, such as the mass of individual atoms and molecules, use an instrument called a *mass spectrometer.* The operation of this device is based on the principle that a charged particle, such as an ion, with a mass m, a charge e, and a velocity v, describes a circular path in a magnetic field H, determined by the equation of motion

$$\frac{mv^2}{r} = Hev,$$

where mv^2/r is actually the *centrifugal force* of the particle. Ions that have the same kinetic energy will describe circles of different radii, depending on the mass to charge (m/e) ratio, or depending only on the mass if all ions have the same charge.

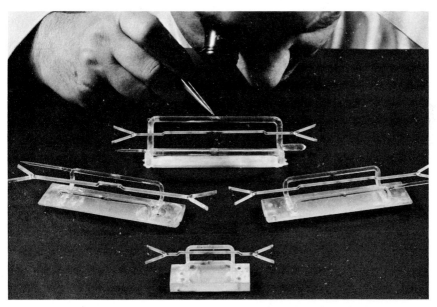

(Westinghouse Research and Development Center)

Frames for quartz microbalances. Specimens and known weights are suspended from wires stretched across the Y's at each end of the beam. The beam pivots on small wires attached to the center of the beam. When in use, the entire assembly is enclosed in a vacuum.

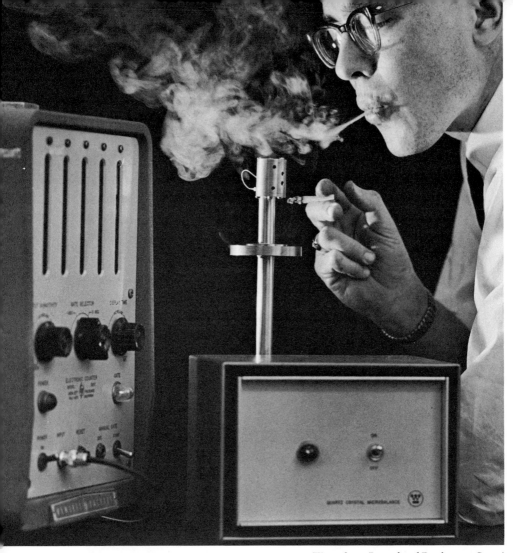

Electronic balance for measuring small weights. A quartz crystal oscillator changes its resonance frequency if its mass changes. Operating on this principle, the balance shown will change its frequency when a mass as minute as that of a layer of gas atoms is added to the surface of the quartz crystal. This change in weight is less than 3×10^{-10} ounces.

The mass spectrometer, shown schematically in Fig. 9.5, consists of an ion source, an analyzer, and a detector. The atoms and molecules are ionized in the ion source, and all are given the same kinetic energy by acceleration through the same voltage difference. This is expressed by the equation

$$\frac{1}{2} mv^2 = eV,$$

90

where V is the voltage. After acceleration, the ions enter the magnetic field, where they are separated according to their angular momentum. The separation is accomplished by two slits, one through which the ions enter the analyzer and which collimates the ion beam, and an exit slit through which the selected ions can reach the detector. The detector may be an *electron multiplier*, which will be described later, or a simple ion collector, where the ion current is measured with a sensitive current meter. The instrument's resolution, or ability to separate ions of different masses, is given by the equation

$$\frac{M_2 - M_1}{M_2} = \frac{r}{S_1 + S_2},$$

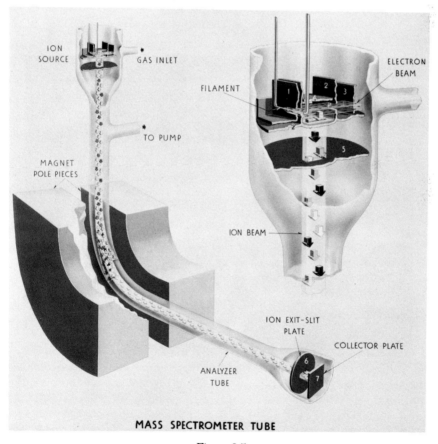

MASS SPECTROMETER TUBE

Figure 9.5

(Courtesy of McMaster University; photo by Tom Bochsler)

Double-focusing mass spectrometer at McMaster University, Toronto. Ion source at the right creates ions which are accelerated through the electrostatic focusing system (to right of panel) where a beam of ions of narrow energy range are selected. This beam is passed through the large semicircular magnet ring (shown at left of control panel). The instrument can determine atomic mass differences of one part in 200,000 atomic mass units.

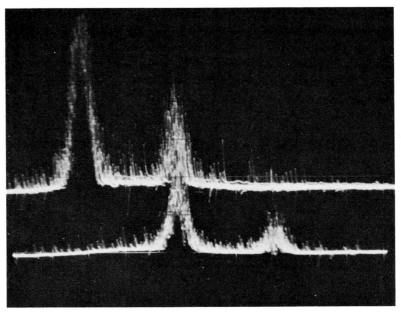

(Courtesy of McMaster University)

Oscilloscope trace of ion currents obtained with McMaster's mass spectrometer. The ion peaks, due to $CD^{114}Cl^{35}$ and $Cd^{112}Cl^{37}$ are split into a double trace and the voltage is adjusted until the larger peak coincides with the smaller one. The voltage required to produce this shift is a measure of the mass difference, in this case 3.4565×10^{-3} atomic mass units, or one part in 42,000.

92

where M_2 and M_1 are two ion species, r is the radius of curvature, and S_1 and S_2 are the widths of the entrance and exit slits, respectively. This is a first-order approximation and holds only for resolving mass differences of less than approximately a hundred atomic mass units. For mass spectrometers of higher resolution, it is necessary to take special precautions in determining the energy of the ions, the shape of the magnetic field, and the design of the slits.

Modern mass spectrometers are able to detect differences in atomic masses of one part in about 25,000. Using 1.6608×10^{-24} as the mass of the hydrogen atom, this means a difference in mass of 1×10^{-28} grams can be detected—less than the mass of an electron. Mass spectrometers, now in the process of construction, should be capable of resolving mass differences of only one part in 10^6 atomic mass units. These instruments will be of great value in determining the structure of the nucleus and studying such subatomic particles as the neutrino.

Detecting Flavor and Odor

10

THE HUMAN BODY functions because of a variety of chemical reactions. Certain of the senses are activated by changes in these chemical reactions, or stimulated by changes in the external chemical environment. The senses of hunger and thirst, for example, are triggered by changes in the body's chemistry. The nose, throat, tongue, eyes, and skin provide a means for detecting changes in the external chemical environment. Our eyes and throat sometimes become irritated by certain chemical vapors, which may or may not be detected by the nose. Although the nose can be an extremely sensitive detector of vapors, it is often unreliable. This is illustrated by the fact that when we first enter a room we may be aware of some distinctive odor, although people who have been in the room for some time no longer detect it. We easily become insensitive to most odors; quantitatively, our sense of smell leaves much to be desired.

Actually, the senses of taste and smell are not completely separable. For example, our sense of taste is affected if we hold our noses, and the loss of a sense of taste and smell is a familiar result of a bad head cold. Although the exact mechanism of these senses is still not fully understood, it is generally believed that the taste buds and the olfactory sensors are activated by chemical reactions. If the tongue is dry, the sense of taste is far less acute, and vapors in the air are believed to be dissolved in the moist mucous lining of the nose, producing chemical solutions that stimulate the olfactory sensors.

Both the sense of taste and the sense of smell vary greatly in their reaction to different substances. Bitter substances are the most effective stimuli for taste. One of the most violent of these, strychnine hydrochloride, is detectable in 4×10^{-15} per cent in water solution. Since the molecular weight of strychnine hydrochloride is 407, this corresponds to a 1×10^{-16} molar solution. One of the most odorous chemicals is ethyl mercaptan; the nose can detect a concentration as small as 3×10^{-9} per cent by weight of this chemical (C_2H_5SH) in air. If we assume that there are about 20 cc of air per sniff, this amounts to approximately 1×10^{10} molecules of ethyl mercaptan to each sniff. It is interesting that ethyl alcohol (C_2H_5OH) is only perceptible in air in concentrations of 0.4 per cent, which means that replacing the oxygen atom in alcohol with a sulfur atom to make mercaptan increases our sensitivity of detection by a hundred million times. The reason for this is still unknown.

It appears that in some cases our sense of smell is an unreliable protection. For example, we can detect the odor of vanillin, used to flavor foods, to 2×10^{-11} per cent, but we cannot detect carbon monoxide at all, although it can cause death in concentrations as small as a few parts per hundred thousand.

Many different chemical sensing devices have been developed for analyzing chemical mixtures. Some of these serve as alarms by sensing the presence of injurious vapors in the air we breathe. Like our sense of smell, these detectors are largely selective, sensitive only to specific chemicals or classes of chemicals.

There are other sensors, however, that can detect a wide range of chemicals, and this quality makes them useful for analytical purposes in measuring the composition of gaseous, liquid, or solid materials. The detection is accomplished with an assortment of spectrographs— emission spectrographs, infrared spectrographs, and mass spectrographs—all of which use a variety of detectors. For example, the emission spectrograph may use a photographic plate, which is a photochemical detector used in this instance to measure chemical composition.

In the emission spectrograph, each excited atom of the substance being analyzed gives off a radiation characteristic of only that particular atom, called its *emission spectrum*. When the emission is in a certain range, it can be detected by the human eye, and we call it light. The light of an ordinary lamp bulb, for example, is the emission from excited tungsten atoms. In the emission spectrograph, the characteristic radiations are sorted and displayed as a series of spectral lines, which are radiations of specific wavelengths. By observing these spectral lines, it is possible to detect the presence of a gas, for example, which may be present in quantities as small as one part in 10^7 or 10^8.

Operation of the infrared spectrograph depends on the ability of molecules to absorb infrared energy, which excites them into rotational or vibrational energy states. Infrared radiation, in a narrow wavelength band, is allowed to pass through the gas to be analyzed. If this radiation is of the proper wavelength to excite the rotational or vibrational energy states of the molecule, some of the energy will be absorbed. An infrared detector, placed opposite the source of infrared energy, monitors the radiation passed through the gas. The unabsorbed radiation, when amplified and recorded on a strip chart recorder, exhibits a tracing of

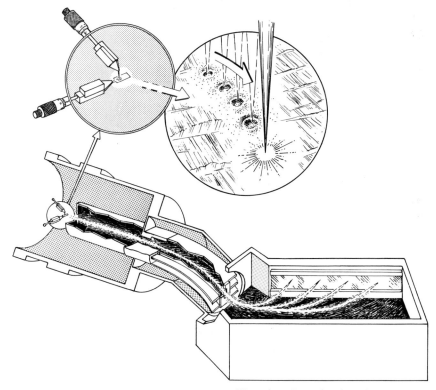

(Westinghouse Research and Development Center)

Schematic drawing of mass spectograph for studying solids. A high frequency spark (shown in insert) produces a small burst of vaporized metallic ions. These ions are sorted by the analyzer according to their mass and are focused on a photographic plate.

(Courtesy of Consolidated Electrodynamics Corporation, Pasadena, California)

A commercial mass spectrometer used for analysis of mixtures of gases and liquids. Such instruments can readily analyze mixtures containing up to fifteen or twenty separate components in only a few minutes, and are routinely used in the chemical and petroleum industries.

successive peaks and valleys. Each molecule has a characteristic tracing, and the tracing produced by a mixture of gases can be analyzed to determine the composition of the mixture. Although the infrared spectrograph is highly sensitive for some molecular gases, it is unsuitable for others and for atomic gases.

In a mass spectrograph, a sensitive electrical detector may be used for final detection, and in this case electric current indicates chemical composition. This instrument, probably the most versatile for gas analysis, depends on the ability of electrons to ionize the molecules. An electron beam of sufficient energy, passing through the gas sample, will separate a molecule into fragments and ionize them. For example,

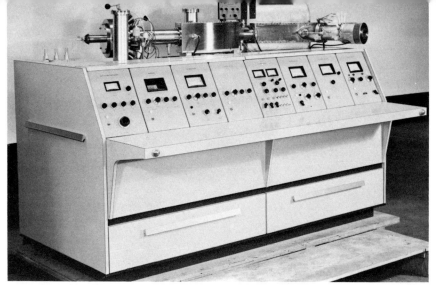

(Courtesy of Consolidated Electrodynamics Corporation, Pasadena, California)

Double focusing mass spectrometer with a high resolution for chemical analysis.

(Courtesy of Consolidated Electrodynamics Corporation, Pasadena, California)

Photoplate from the double focusing mass spectrometer, illustrating the advantages of high resolution. Lines on the photographic film are produced by ions of different masses. The single line at left is mass 27.0235 produced by a $C_2H_3^+$ ion. Triplet at right is 27.9949 from CO^+, 28.0061 from N_2^+, and 28.0313 from $C_2H_4^+$. High resolution allows separate determination of CO, N_2, and the hydrocarbon. Intensity of the lines is proportional to the percentage composition.

99

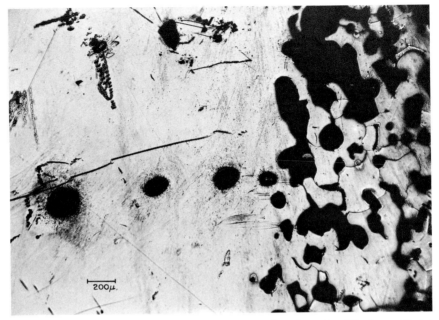

(Westinghouse Research and Development Center)

An example of the use of the mass spectograph. A diffusion zone in a semiconductor is studied by a series of sparks proceeding across the zone. The mass spectra of each spot show composition changes. It is possible to detect changes of atomic concentrations of certain elements to one part in 10^6 atoms.

CO will be dissociated and ionized into C^+ and O^+, and H_2O will be separated into H_2^+ and O^+, as well as OH^+ and H^+. Likewise, a more complicated molecule such as that of propane will be dissociated into all the possible combinations of carbon and hydrogen: $C_3H_8^+$, $C_3H_7^+$, $C_3H_6^+$, $C_3H_5^+$, $C_2H_5^+$, $C_2H_4^+$, $C_2H_3^+$, CH_3^+, CH_2^+, CH^+, C^+, H_2^+, and H^+. The mass spectrograph (or spectrometer) accelerates these ions, and allows them to pass through a magnetic field, where they are separated according to their relative molecular weights. A detector can then detect each kind of ion separately; the intensity of each will be different. Thus, for propane (C_3H_8) there is a characteristic mass spectrum, consisting of the various ion species. If the characteristic spectrum of each molecule is known, it is almost always possible to analyze a complicated mixture of gases. In the chemical and petroleum industries, mass spectrometry is routinely used to analyze mixtures containing

100

twenty or more components. These instruments, coupled with new computing techniques, make it possible for a chemist to perform such analyses in a few minutes, and can often detect the presence of atomic impurities of 1 part in 10^8.

In a modern laboratory, the analytical section usually contains all three of the spectrographs described above, as well as other analytical instruments, such as gas chromatographs and x-ray spectrometers.

We cannot attempt to describe here the great variety of chemical analytical methods available. However today, with the widening development of solid state physics, it becomes increasingly important to detect and measure ever smaller concentrations of atoms and molecules. For example, when pure silicon or germanium crystals are being grown, the deliberate introduction of impurities of less than 1 part in 10^8 can drastically alter the performance of a semiconductor device.

Beyond the Limits of Vision

11

SIGHT, undoubtedly man's most valuable means of receiving information about his environment, is accomplished with light sensors located in our eyes. These sensors are activated by electromagnetic radiation in the wavelength region from 4,000 to 7,000 angstrom units. Since an angstrom unit is 1×10^{-8} cm, our visible range spans the wavelength region from 0.0004 cm at the violet end of the color spectrum to 0.0007 cm at the red end.

Electromagnetic waves are transverse, characterized by vibratory motion at right angles to the direction of the wave propagation. This motion can be simulated by tying one end of a rope to an object, and moving the other end quickly up and down. Waves can be seen to move along the rope horizontally, although each particle of the rope moves successively in a vertical direction. When the free end is given a quick flip up and down, a pulse is seen to travel along the rope; when the free end is shaken in a regular rhythm, series of pulses move along the rope, producing waves. A marker, tied to the rope, will move only up and down. The wavelength is determined by the distance between two adjacent crests or hollows (maxima or minima), or any other two points in corresponding adjacent positions. The faster the rope vibrates, the more waves per unit length, or the shorter the wavelength. The frequency of the waves, ν (number of waves per unit time), and the wavelength, λ, is given by

$$\nu\lambda = c, \text{ or} \left(\frac{\text{waves}}{\text{time}}\right)\left(\frac{\text{length}}{\text{waves}}\right) = \frac{\text{length}}{\text{time}} = \text{velocity}.$$

For electromagnetic radiation, c of course is the velocity of light, equal to 3×10^{10} cm/sec, or 186,000 mi/sec.

Exactly how the eye detects light is not known. There are several theories that attempt to explain the phenomenon of sight, and although these differ slightly, there is general agreement that the sense of sight is a combination of photochemical and photoelectric phenomena. Details of this complex subject are not pertinent to our present discussion, but a few facts will be of interest. The light-sensitive receptors are located in the retina of the eye. The dimension of each receptor is between two and four microns (.002 to .004 millimeters). Thus, in the center of the retina where the highest resolution is attained, there are about 50,000 to 100,000 receptors per square millimeter. The resolution is a measure of the amount of detail we can see, and depends on the density of receptors per unit area. The normal eye can resolve two points separated by a visual angle of one minute. This is determined by a distance on the retina of about .0044 millimeters, a little more than the diameter of a cone receptor. If two points of an object stimulate a single receptor, or two adjacent receptors, they cannot be distinguished. However, if these two points stimulate two receptors that are separated by one unstimulated receptor, the eye can distinguish them as two separate points. Of course, this is an oversimplification of the resolution of the human eye, since movements of the head or of the eye itself would shift a point of illumination over several receptors in the retina. Thus, the resolving ability is based on some manner of average intensities over adjacent receptors.

The eye contains elements with widely varying degrees of sensitivity, so the dynamic range is many orders of magnitude. From the threshold of perception to full sunlight, the range of intensities is 1 to 10^{10}. In addition, the sensors themselves differ, responding in different ways and being activated by radiation of different wavelengths. Some sensors are most responsive to radiation that produces blue light; some to radiation that produces yellow light; some to radiation that produces red light. These sensors are grouped in threes over the retina, and they determine our color perception. The same scheme has been copied in color television tubes.

Light acts on certain chemicals in the receptors, and produces a kind of chemical bleaching action. This, in turn, produces electrical impulses, which pass through the optic nerve to the brain. If more light is prevented from reaching the eye, the bleached chemical returns

104

to its normal state. Thus, the sensitive elements are continually renewable, unlike photographic film which, once exposed, cannot be reactivated. But the renewal process of sight takes time, and thus we persist in seeing the image of a bright light for a while after we look away from it, or close our eyes. So much of the chemical has been bleached, it takes time to return to its unbleached state. Conversely, we can see in the dark once our eyes have become adapted, because they have had an opportunity to store up a large amount of unbleached chemical. At this point, the human eye can detect visible light energy equivalent to one *photon*, a quantum of electromagnetic energy. This suggests that it is an extremely sensitive detector, but actually, like other human sensors, it is not very reliable as a quantitative instrument and it has a limited frequency response. This limitation is graphically illustrated in Fig. 11.1, which shows the complete electromagnetic spectrum as it is known today. Actually there is no definite long wavelength boundary, since radiation is produced by any oscillating charge no matter how slow the oscillation. For example, electrical power is generated at 60 cy/sec, and this gives rise to radiation whose wavelength is about 5×10^8 cm (5×10^3 kilometers).

The ability to detect radiation depends on the energy per unit area impinging on the sensor. Energy per unit time is usually expressed in *watts*, one watt being equal to 10^7 ergs/sec. An *erg* is work produced by a force of one *dyne*, acting through a distance of one *centimeter*. In these discussions, we will describe energy in watts, since this is the most familiar unit. An ordinary incandescent light bulb, rated 60 watts, consumes 60 watts of power. However, only about 3 per cent, or 2 watts, is radiated as energy detectable to the eye. This energy is radiated uniformly in all directions, and yet a 60-watt bulb can easily be seen by the human eye at a distance of 25 miles, or about 40 kilometers. This means that the light intensity is distributed uniformly on a sphere 25 miles in radius, and the surface area of this sphere is about 2×10^{14} square centimeters. Assuming that the pupil of the eye has an area of about one square centimeter, the eye is then detecting 1×10^{-14} watts from the light bulb.

Radiant energy of very small amounts is best described in terms of *quanta*. Light exhibits a dualistic nature; that is, it possesses some properties that can be described by wave motion, and others that can

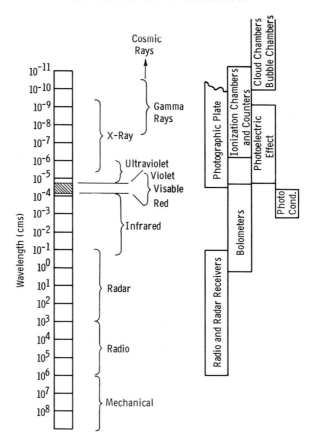

Figure 11.1

best be described by the motion of particles. An explanation of the properties of radiation that combines both these descriptions is called *wave,* or *quantum, mechanics.* According to this explanation, energy of radiation is considered to be propagated in discrete amounts, called quanta. A quantum of energy is the smallest amount possible for a particle of radiation with a wavelength λ, and is given by the relationship

$$E = \frac{hc}{\lambda},$$

where c is the velocity of light, and h is Planck's constant, equal to 6.624×10^{-27} erg/sec. For long wavelengths, the energy per quantum

106

is small; for short wavelengths, the energy per quantum is large. For example, using $c = 3 \times 10^{10}$ cm/sec, the energy in a quantum of radiation for a radio wave ($\lambda = 10^4$ cm) is 2×10^{-20} ergs. This much energy falling per second on a sensor is equivalent to 2×10^{-27} watts. At the other end of the spectrum, a quantum of x-ray radiation with a wavelength of about 1×10^{-9} centimeters has an energy of approximately 2×10^{-7} ergs. This quantum per second is equivalent to 2×10^{-12} watts, and contains 10^{15} times as much energy as a radio wave.

Coming back to the 60-watt light bulb 25 miles (or about 40 kilometers) away, we note that the energy reaching the eye is 10^{-14} watts. As we said before, the human eye can detect one photon of radiation in the visible region. If its wavelength is 5×10^{-5} centimeters (green light), it has an energy equal to about 4×10^{-12} ergs, which amounts to an energy of 4×10^{-19} watts in one second. The light bulb is delivering 10^5 times more energy than the lower limit of detection. This means that the light bulb could be 2,500 miles away (about 4,000 kilometers), and still be detected.

From the visible portion of the electromagnetic spectrum, scientists have been able to extend their investigation to both longer and shorter wavelengths by using a variety of sensors.

At the beginning of the nineteenth century, experiments established the existence of radiation beyond the violet end of the visible spectrum, and this came to be known as the *ultraviolet* region. The existence of x rays had been established by the turn of the century. Many detectors now cover a wide range from the infrared through the x-ray region.

The detection of infrared radiation is as old as man himself. The first cave dweller undoubtedly noticed that rocks heated by a fire continued to give off heat after all visible signs of fire had disappeared. Not until about 1800, however, was heat radiation recognized as an extension of visible radiation—invisible, but detectable by temperature sensors in the skin. Thermal effects, such as the heating of thermometers or thermocouples, were used in early experiments to determine the wave nature of this radiation.

Photographic film is one of the most widely used detectors of electromagnetic radiation. Its use, originally confined to the visible region, has now been extended into the x-ray region and even into the near infrared. This use of photographic film is based on the ability of a photon to produce a chemical change in a molecule, which is a quantum effect. In 1922 Albert Einstein postulated the principle of photochemical equivalence, which states that in a photochemical process, the decomposition of one molecule requires one quantum of energy, $h\lambda/c$ (λ depending on the particular molecule).

A modern photographic plate depends on the dissociation of silver salts, such as AgBr or AgCl, dispensed in a thin film of gelatin. Photons, striking the silver salts, change them so that the developer reduces the salts to metallic silver. Technical advances have reduced exposure times for comparable light intensities from hours, required in 1826, to less than one-thousandth of a second for modern films.

Using photographic plates is an *integrating* method, and this is a great advantage. Since each photon produces a chemical change in the silver-salt molecule, it is possible to expose the film for long periods of time, and thus accumulate the effects of many photons. For example, by making long exposures of radiation from the sky, astronomers have been able to see literally millions of stars, impossible to detect by direct observation through a telescope. More recent exposures with sensitive color film have opened up exciting new areas of investigation of the universe.

Since the photochemical effect is quantum in nature, as we have mentioned, it is not useful for the long-wavelength portion of the electromagnetic spectrum, where the energy per quantum is small. For this region it is necessary to use other detectors, such as bolometers, thermocouples, and the radio tube. In the broadest sense, these are photoelectric devices in which electromagnetic radiation produces an electric current.

In the long-wavelength region of the spectrum are the familiar radio and television waves, for which the sensing element is a receiving tube. The antenna acts like the lens of an eye, in that it gathers the energy from a wide area and focuses it into a small one. This is an important function, since the energy incident per unit area determines the ability to detect the radiation. Thus, as the wavelength becomes longer and the energy per photon becomes smaller, a large antenna or energy-gathering system is needed.

The radio waves intercepted by the antenna interact with the electrons in a metal conductor and set up minute voltage differences, which

(Courtesy of Allegheny Observatory, Pittsburgh, Pa.)

Photochemical sensor; photographic film used for integrating weak signals. A star cluster, photographed with a telescope using a one-minute exposure (*A*), and a 28 minute exposure (*B*) which reveals many more stars.

appear on the control grid of a receiving tube. The receiving tube has a source of electrons, and these leave a cathode, flow past the control grid and reach the anode. The number of electrons that reach the anode (positive electrode) depends on the voltage of the control grid. A small change in the grid voltage produces a large change in the electron current. Since the electrons move very fast, the tube can follow rapid voltage changes in the control grid circuit. For radar waves, these changes are many billions of times per second. Wavelengths equal to those employed in commercial short-wave radio can be detected by a modern receiver even though the signals are of a strength equivalent to 10^{-16} watts.

Infrared or heat waves are somewhat shorter in wavelength than radio waves. Detection of infrared waves for military surveillance is currently receiving a good deal of scientific attention. Devices aptly called "snooperscopes" allow any warm object to be detected. Antimissile or antiaircraft missiles can be guided by detectors that sense infrared radiation given off by the heat from engines. Equipped with an infrared camera, a satellite is able to take photographs through a slight haze cover, or even at night.

The simplest type of infrared detector, the thermocouple, is thermoelectric. The thermoelectric effect (Seebeck, 1822) is associated with the development of a voltage across the junction of two metals whose *work functions* are different. (The work function is the amount of energy required to remove an electron out of the metal surface.) This voltage is proportional to the temperature of the junction with respect to the voltage of a reference junction. The voltage (emf) generated is thus given by

$$\text{emf} = K(T_2 - T_1),$$

where K is a constant dependent on the combination of metals, and T is the temperature of the respective junctions. The principle is illustrated in Fig. 11.2. Suppose we have a ring, composed of two metals A and B, such as copper and iron, joined at the two junctions. We now apply heat to junction 2. Since copper is a good electrical conductor, the electrons move quite freely, and the distribution of conduction electrons is not changed appreciably. Iron, on the other hand, is not such a good conductor; thus, the electrons that are driven from the

110

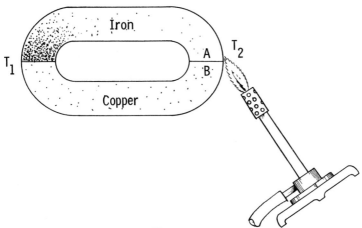

Figure 11.2

hot junction find it harder to get back, and therefore they pile up at the cold end. This difference in the electron population results in a voltage difference between the two junctions, and if the difference in voltage is sufficient to overcome the work function of the metals, an electric current will flow. The amount of voltage depends on the work functions of the metals and on the temperature difference. A large voltage difference can be obtained by placing many thermocouples in series; this is called a *thermopile*. With very thin wires and many such junctions in series, a detector can be made sensitive enough to detect the radiation from a candle ten miles away.

The *bolometer,* a thermoresistive detector, is another type of infrared detector that depends on the radiation producing an electrical effect. This device operates on the change of electrical resistivity as a function of temperature. The thermal coefficient C of a material is given by

$$C = \frac{1}{\rho}\frac{d\rho}{dT},$$

where $d\rho/dT$ represents the change in resistivity, ρ, as a function of temperature.

For metals, the resistivity is given by $\rho = \rho_0\,(1 + \alpha T)$, where ρ_0 is the resistivity at $0°C$. For semiconductors, the resistivity is proportional to $\exp\,(eE_g/kT)$, where E_g is the activation energy, k is the Boltzmann constant, and T is the temperature.

111

(Courtesy of Haller, Raymond and Brown, Inc.)

Picture of Manhattan Island, New York City, taken at night with an infra red detector and camera. Warm objects are light, cold objects dark.

In modern bolometers, very thin films are prepared with special attention to blackness and surface roughness so that they will be essentially perfect absorbers of radiation of all wavelengths. The advantage of the bolometer is its constant response over the entire wavelength range, from ultraviolet to far infrared, since it is not selective to photons of different wavelengths. A modern bolometer will detect radiation with power as small as 10^{-9} watts.

A special category of infrared detectors is closely allied to the bolometer. However, this group depends on the absorption of the radiant energy to change the physical dimensions of the detector. The most common is the ordinary mercury thermometer, in which expansion of a volume of mercury is used to detect the energy falling on the thermometer. Gas thermometers, also for the detection of heat energy, are useful over a wider range of temperature than are the liquid thermometers, and they are effective down to liquid-helium temperatures.

A kind of gas thermometer called a *Golay cell* has been developed for detecting minute amounts of energy in the infrared region. As shown in Fig. 11.3, the infrared radiation falls on an absorbing film F which increases in temperature, thus heating the gas enclosed in a small volume V. The opposite side of V is a thin membrane M. When heated, the gas expands and increases the pressure, thus increasing the force on the membrane, which deflects it slightly. Attached to the membrane is a grid G_1 composed of alternate transparent and opaque lines of equal width, mounted parallel to a fixed grid G_2 of similar design. A lens system allows parallel light from the light source to pass through the grids and to be focused on a photoelectric cell. When the grids are adjusted to coincide, the photocell receives the maximum intensity and yields the maximum electric current. If G_1 moves with respect to

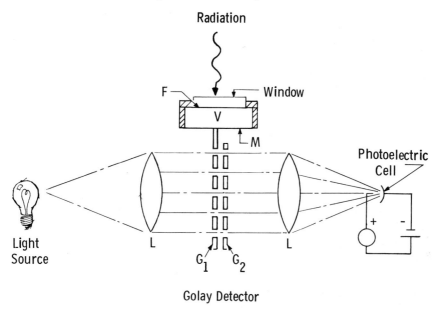

Golay Detector

Figure 11.3

G_2, the light intensity is diminished, and so is the electric current. When G_1 moves a distance equal to the width of one spacing, the light is shut off from the photocell, and the current drops to zero. Thus, by making the grid spacing sufficiently fine, extremely small distances can be measured. With modern Golay detectors, it is possible to detect radiant power in the infrared region as small as 10^{-10} watts.

For the short infrared and the visible regions, there are two kinds of photoelectric detectors, one of which is used in connection with the Golay cell.

Photoelectric effects, like photochemical effects, are quantum in nature and are governed by the relation

$$\frac{hc}{\lambda} = eE_\omega,$$

where h is Planck's constant, c the velocity of light, λ the wavelength, e the electronic charge, and E_ω the activation energy. This is a quantum effect, because unless hc/λ exceeds E_ω nothing happens. There are two photoelectric effects depending on the E_ω involved. The first is an external effect, called *photoelectric emission*, in which an electron

(Westinghouse Research and Development Center)

A picture of two men taken with the Astracon at night, with only starlight for illumination.

is ejected from the surface of the detector and is equivalent to the work function. The second is the *photoconductive* effect, in which the radiation falling on the material produces an appreciable change in its electrical conductivity. These two effects are explained graphically in Fig. 11.4.

Metals are able to conduct electricity easily, because they have a large number of free or conduction electrons, which can move freely from one atom to another within the material. There are also other electrons, called *valence* or *bound* electrons, associated with each atom. These electrons require a certain amount of energy to escape the atom, and are said to be trapped. We speak of them as being trapped in potential wells, very much like a ball resting in a depression.

In part *a* of Fig. 11.4, a metal conductor is pictured in simple terms.

114

The open circles in the wells indicate bound or trapped electrons; the solid circles are free, or conduction, electrons. If a voltage is applied to the ends of this conductor, the free electrons can flow to the positive electrode because they do not have to overcome any potential barrier. However, these electrons cannot escape out of the surface of the metal, because there is a potential barrier whose height is given by φ. This barrier is called the *work function.* For an electron to escape the metal, it must receive enough energy to overcome the barrier potential φ which corresponds to E_ω in the preceding equation for the first of the two photoelectric effects. If a photon with an energy hc/λ greater than $e\varphi$ is absorbed by a conduction electron, this electron may escape from the metal with a velocity given by the expression

$$\tfrac{1}{2}\,mv^2 = \frac{hc}{\lambda} - e\varphi,$$

where m is the mass of the electron and v is its velocity. We can see from part a of Fig. 11.4 that a good deal more energy is required to

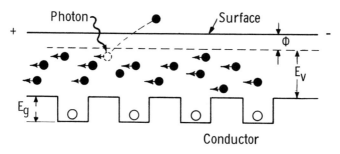

a. Photoemission

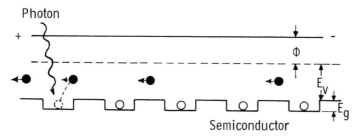

b. Photoconduction

Figure 11.4

liberate a trapped electron from the surface, since this energy must be equal to

$$e(E_g + E_v + \varphi),$$

where E_g is the energy required to lift a trapped valence electron to the lowest energy state of the conduction electron and E_v is the energy range a conduction electron may possess. In a photoemissive detector, the least energetic photon that can be detected is determined by φ, and for this reason photoemissive surfaces are usually those with low work functions.

If the photon gives its energy to a trapped electron, this electron is said to be raised from the energy state of the valence electron to that of the conduction electron, which is described by the photoconductivity effect illustrated in part b of Fig. 11.4.

As the name implies, photoconductivity is the production of electrical conductivity by the action of photons. This effect is unimportant in conductors, because conductivity is already high and minute charges cannot be detected. However, in a class of materials called *semiconductors* the effect may be significant. The difference between a semiconductor and a conductor may be seen by comparing the two parts of Fig. 11.4. In conductors there are many free electrons, but in semiconductors, although there are few free electrons, it is possible to make the traps shallow, so that E_g is small, which means the photon needs to have an energy $hc/\lambda \geq eE_g$. The work function φ may be greater than that for a conductor, but this is of no consequence in photoconductors. Of course, if the photon has sufficient energy, it may also eject electrons in the same manner as a conductor. There are several varieties of photoconductors that depend on the nature of the traps.

Cesium, the conductor with the lowest work function, requires a photon of about 4,000 angstroms (violet) wavelength, or an energy of about 4.5×10^{-12} ergs, to eject an electron. Photoconductors, on the other hand, can be made with such very shallow traps that they can detect radiation in the far infrared. These detectors are very temperature-sensitive, of course, and some are so sensitive in this respect that it is necessary to cool them to liquid-helium temperatures before they can be used effectively.

Photoemission detectors that combine photoelectric emission with secondary electron emission are extremely sensitive; such devices are

116

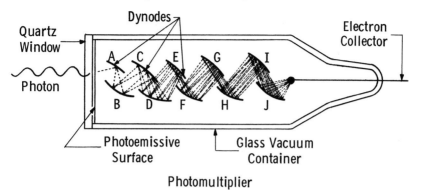

Photomultiplier

Figure 11.5

called *photomultipliers*. Secondary electron emission is similar to photoelectron emission: an energetic electron that strikes a surface gives up its kinetic energy to the electrons in the surface, causing them to be ejected. The number ejected depends on the kinetic energy of the incident electron and on the nature of the material. Metallurgists have recently developed certain alloys which, properly treated, can be made to yield up to 10 to 15 electrons for each striking electron with an impact energy of 250 electron volts. An *electron volt* is the kinetic energy acquired by an electron accelerated through a potential difference of one volt. This is equivalent to 1.6×10^{-12} ergs, which corresponds to a photon with a wavelength of 12,336 angstroms, or .00012 cm.

A photomultiplier is illustrated in Fig. 11.5. The photons to be detected are allowed to fall on a quartz plate, which will not absorb them. The inside surface of the quartz is coated with a thin layer of metal, such as a cesium compound. The photon is absorbed by the cesium compound, and ejects a photoelectron. This electron is accelerated toward the first multiplier plate, called a *dynode*. Striking the dynode, the electron liberates, for example, two electrons. Each of these is accelerated to the second dynode, where each liberates two electrons. The resulting four electrons are accelerated to the third dynode, where they liberate eight electrons, and so on. Thus, in an electron multiplier, the final number of electrons reaching the collector is given by the expression

$$N_e = (\alpha)^n,$$

117

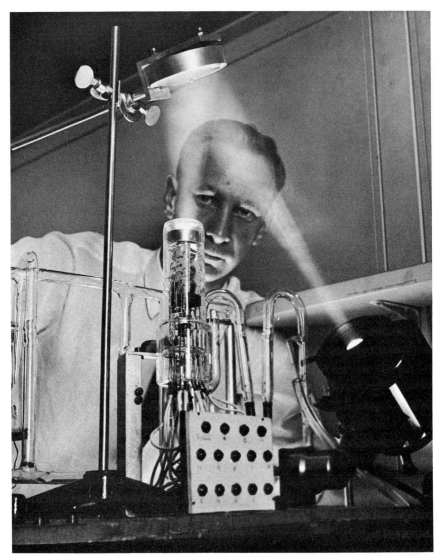

(Westinghouse Research and Development Center)

Photomultiplier ion gauge, a photoelectric sensor for measuring gas pressure. Ultraviolet light focused on the first dynode liberates electrons which in turn are accelerated to the second plate, producing more electrons. After ten or fifteen stages of amplification, the electrons are passed through an ionization chamber where gases present are ionized and the ion current is measured. Ion current is thus a measure of gas pressure, and such a gauge can measure less than one millionth of a millionth (10^{-12}) atmospheres.

118

where α is the number of electrons liberated per stage, and n is the number of stages. Modern multipliers, with 15 to 20 steps of amplification, obtain 10^8 electrons for each incident electron at the first stage. With these multipliers, it is possible to detect a single photon whose energy is sufficiently high to liberate a photoelectron.

Charged particles may also be detected with this device; by removing the quartz window, positive ions or electrons can be made to strike the first multiplier dynode. With modern multipliers, it is possible to detect fewer than one charged particle per minute striking the first dynode.

When the energy of the photons reaches about 10 electron volts (x-ray region), the photons produce a different photoelectric effect, called *photoionization*. In photoionization, the photon, on striking an atom or molecule, has sufficient energy to liberate an electron, producing a free electron and a positive ion. Photoionization is used in an assortment of detectors which can sense radiation from the violet region of the electromagnetic spectrum (about 3.5 ev) to the shortest

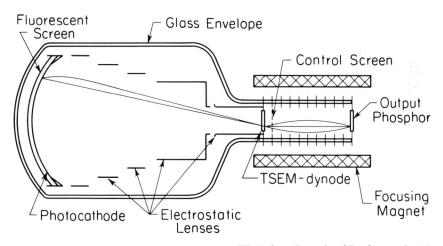

(Westinghouse Research and Development Center)

Image intensifier tube, shown schematically. X rays striking the fluorescent screen liberate electrons from the photocathode. These electrons are focused by electrostatic lenses onto the transmission secondary electron multiplier (TSEM) where electron signals are multiplied and strike the output phosphor, producing visible light. A magnetic field allows the image to be transmitted without distortion.

119

(Westinghouse Research and Development Center)

Photon-electron-Photon sensor. An example of how sensors are combined into a new instrument. X rays passing through metal produce a diffraction pattern on the large end of the tube. These x rays (photons) liberate electrons which are focused on the first stage of a transmission electron multiplier. Several stages of amplification can be obtained without loss of detail in the original pattern. The final stage allows the electrons to strike a phosphor which produces visible light. Thus in effect the observer sees the x rays; such a sensor also allows x-ray moving pictures to be made.

wavelengths of the cosmic rays, where energies are measured in billions of electron volts. Radiation at these energies, with corresponding wavelengths less than one angstrom (10^{-8} cm), can penetrate many meters of solid matter. For example, cosmic rays originating in outer space can be detected in caves and shallow mines, after having penetrated through the atmosphere and many feet of rock.

The wavelength of a quantum of cosmic ray may be less than 10^{-12} cm, a dimension comparable to that of an atomic nucleus. Therefore, when these rays are intercepted by a nucleus they produce great devastation and the nucleus flies apart in several energetic fragments. Nuclear debris particles may be mesons, protons, neutrons, neutrinos, or gamma rays; positively charged, negatively charged, or neutral. Nuclear scientists, in an effort to solve the mystery of the nucleus and perhaps also the origin of cosmic rays, have built tremendous atom smashers, which will produce "bullets" with energies of billions of electron volts (BeV) to fire at atomic nuclei.

(Westinghouse Research and Development Center)

"Astracon" tube for light amplification. Photons liberate electrons from a photocathode and these are accelerated to strike a thin membrane where several electrons are ejected from the back surface. Nine stages of electron magnification are achieved and electrons strike a phosphor where photons in the visible range are liberated. Since an axial magnetic field keeps the electrons in line, the image is transferred from end to end without distortion. Photon amplification of 100,000 at 4,200 Å can be obtained.

The simplest device for detecting photoionization is an ionization chamber, shown in Fig. 11.6. This is a metal box, equipped inside with an insulated electrode maintained at a suitable potential with respect to the walls. If photons such as x rays are to be detected, the box may be fitted with a thin window. Photons entering the chamber ionize the gas. Under the influence of the applied voltage difference, the electrons and ions are accelerated to the appropriate electrodes. A sensitive current meter, such as a galvanometer, is used to measure the current.

A special adaptation of this device is the Geiger-Mueller counter, shown in Fig. 11.7. Inside a thin-walled metal cylinder, there is a fine wire electrically insulated from the container, which is filled with a suitable gas at a pressure determined by the particular use. An electrical potential of several thousand volts, just short of the voltage that would produce an electrical discharge, is applied between the cylinder and the wire. If radiation now penetrates the cylinder wall and enters the counter, it ionizes one or more molecules. The electrons produced by this primary ionization event are accelerated by the action of the large electric field, and acquire enough energy to produce additional electron-ion pairs. This results in an electrical discharge. Provided a suitable gas is used and the voltage differences are properly adjusted, it is possible to limit this discharge to a very short pulse, which may be

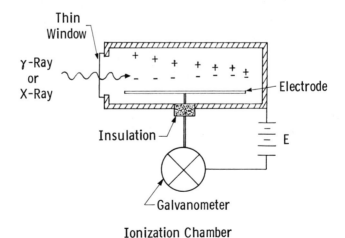

Ionization Chamber

Figure 11.6

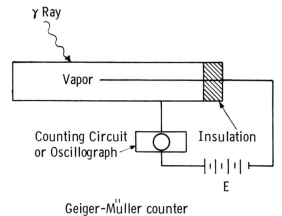

Geiger-Müller counter

Figure 11.7

displayed on a cathode ray oscilloscope or used to activate a counting circuit. Thus, it is possible to count separate gamma rays or other ionizing particles, the counting rate being an indication of the level of radiation. This type of detection is suitable for x rays and cosmic rays.

Cosmic rays, originating in outer space, are the most energetic form of radiation. We do not know the energy limit of cosmic rays, but so far scientists have evidence of cosmic rays with 10^{19} electron volts.

Counters are used not only to detect but also to measure the direction and energy of many such high-energy particles. Fig. 11.8 shows schematically how this may be done. *A*, *B*, and *C* are three counters, placed in a line with lead foil between them, and interconnected so that the radiation is not counted unless all three counters fire simultaneously. This process is called *coincidence counting*, and is frequently used to detect events that occur in experiments dealing with nuclear physics. In our diagram, only a vertical gamma ray would trigger all three counters. By varying foil thicknesses, it is possible to prevent one or more counters from firing. In this way a measure of the initial energy of radiation can be obtained, provided the absorption coefficient of the foil is known.

Scientists today send packages of various counters aloft in balloons and satellites to study radiation entering the upper atmosphere from space. The existence of intense bands of radiation surrounding the earth was detected when the first satellites were launched.

123

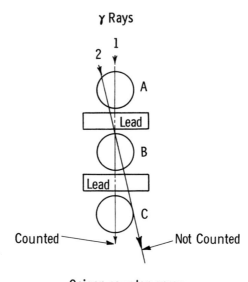

Geiger counter array

Figure 11.8

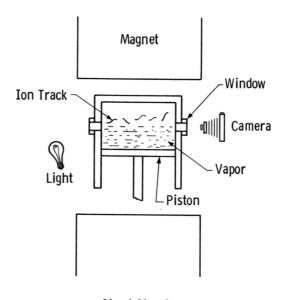

Cloud Chamber

Figure 11.9

Two other instruments, the cloud chamber and the bubble chamber, are also used to study high-energy radiation. The principle of the cloud chamber is shown in Fig. 11.9. The device employs a cylinder and a piston that can be moved quickly. A suitable liquid which will produce a vapor is admitted to the cylinder and slowly compressed. The gas becomes saturated with the vapor. If the piston is now released quickly, the gas is cooled and hence the over-saturated vapor condenses in a fine fog or cloud. When a high-energy particle or gamma ray passes through the chamber, it produces a track of ionization. If ions are created in the chamber, the vapor will condense around them, forming minute droplets. When a strong light is reflected from these droplets, it is possible to photograph the ionization track left by the particle.

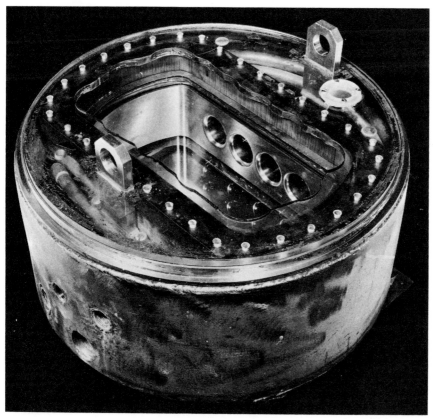

(Courtesy of Lawrence Radiation Laboratory, University of California, Berkeley, California)
Cloud chamber used for the detection of high energy particles.

If we place the cloud chamber in a magnetic field, the ionization track will be either curved or straight, depending on whether the particle producing the ionization is electrically charged or neutral. From the direction of curvature in a magnetic field of known orientation, it is possible to determine if the charge is positive or negative. A charged particle will describe a circular orbit in a magnetic field, as mentioned before, and the radius of curvature is related to its energy by the equation

$$mv^2/r = He\,v,$$

where m is the mass of the particle, v is its velocity, r is the radius of curvature, e is the particle's charge, and H is the magnetic field. Of

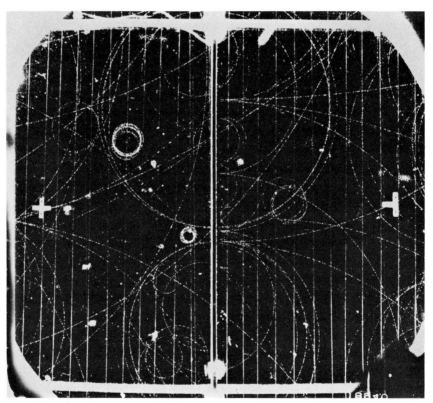

(Courtesy of Lawrence Radiation Laboratory, University of California)

Particle tracks in an expansion-type cloud chamber. The small circles are made by low energy particles, the larger circles by particles of higher energy. Particles of positive charge are bent to the right and those of negative charge to the left.

course, as the particle produces ionization, it loses some of its initial energy, and so its path will not be a perfect circle but part of a spiral orbit. In many instances, where both the mass and the initial kinetic energy are unknown, identification becomes extremely difficult.

For particles of very high energy even the cloud chamber becomes inadequate, since it is clear that identification can be made only when an appreciable portion of energy is lost through ionization. In an instrument like the cloud chamber, ionization is produced in a gas, where not many ionizing collisions can take place per unit length of path. In order to increase the energy loss per unit length, it is necessary to use a liquid or a solid.

The bubble chamber is a device that uses a liquid; the instrument illustrated in Fig. 11.10 uses liquid hydrogen. The liquid hydrogen fills a thermally insulated container, slightly pressurized so that bubbles caused by evaporation from the heat of the walls are few and occur only at the surface of the liquid. If the high-energy particle now passes through the liquid, it makes many collisions per unit path, and the energy loss goes into evaporating the hydrogen. Thus, a series of minute hydrogen bubbles condenses around the ions that are created along the path of the particle, and when properly illuminated, these bubbles can be photographed. The use of a magnetic field makes it possible to determine if the incoming particle possesses a positive, negative, or neutral charge.

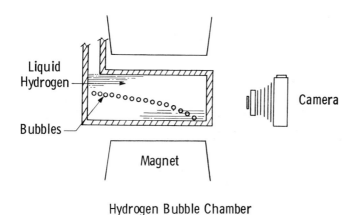

Hydrogen Bubble Chamber

Figure 11.10

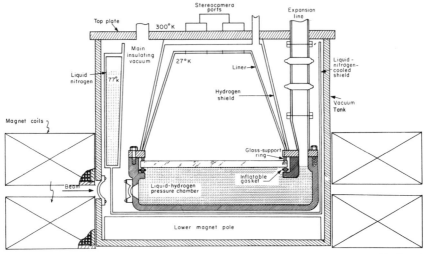

(Courtesy of Lawrence Radiation Laboratory, University of California)

Diagram of major parts of the hydrogen bubble chamber.

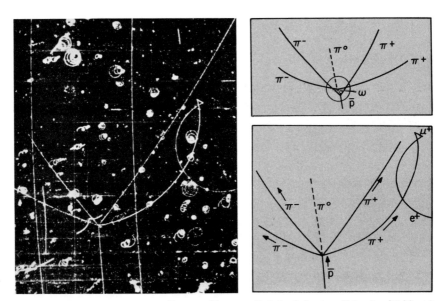

(Courtesy of Lawrence Radiation Laboratory, University of California)

Photograph of an annihilation event in the hydrogen bubble chamber. An antiproton
has disintegrated into four charged mesons, whose tracks are shown in the upper diagram; a neutral meson is indicated by the dashed line. One of the π^+ mesons later
produces a μ^+ meson which in turn disintegrates, producing a positron (e^+) whose
track is the circle of shorter radius. The small corkscrew spirals are low energy
electrons.

128

(Courtesy of Lawrence Radiation Laboratory, University of California)

A 72-inch hydrogen bubble chamber at the Lawrence Radiation Laboratory.

The *scintillation counter* is a special kind of photoelectric detector, or really a photo-photoelectric detector. When a very high-energy photon is absorbed by a crystal, it excites the atoms in the crystal, causing them to radiate photons of lower energy. Thus, one high-energy photon produces several photons of lower energy, and these escape the crystal and strike the photoelectric surface of an electron multiplier, as described earlier. Liquids may be used as well as crystals to produce the scintillations that excite the electron multiplier.

The devices we have been discussing are typical of a series designed to extend man's ability to detect radiation beyond the narrow wavelength of visible light. With improved technology, the boundaries imposed by human limitations continue to be pushed outward into the vast range of energies at both ends of the spectrum.

Space, Motion, and Time

12

OUR SENSES of space, motion, and the passage of time rely on no one sense organ, but rather on some special combination of certain primary senses. As we move about in our environment, for example, we are conscious of moving; the scenery changes, and at times we even become lost, not knowing where we are in relation to familiar landmarks. Over the centuries man has devised numerous means for determining where he is at all times, so that he can move with confidence from one point to another in space. A method of navigation has evolved from a primitive look at the sun, moon, and stars, to a precise measurement of man's own position in relation to the stars.

In order to determine the location of any object in space, it is necessary to measure distances or lengths with precision. As discussed in an earlier section, the need for precise measurements led to the development of a series of units for calculating distances and elevations. From body dimensions came measuring sticks or rulers. The ruler was a straight stick divided into a series of arbitrary distances. As man needed to know distances more exactly, he divided his scale into finer and finer bits. Then, in order to determine the distance between two bits on a scale, the vernier scale was developed for reading the linear scale more accurately. In this device a sliding scale is marked in 10 divisions, equal to 9 divisions of the fixed scale. For example, if the 0 mark on the vernier scale coincides with the 0 mark on the fixed scale, the tenth mark on the vernier or movable scale will coincide with the ninth mark from zero on the fixed scale. If the vernier scale is now moved slightly, some mark between 0 and 10 on this movable scale will coincide with a mark on the fixed scale. This mark determines the fraction of the distance moved between two successive marks on the fixed scale. For example, if the third mark on the vernier scale coincides with a mark on the

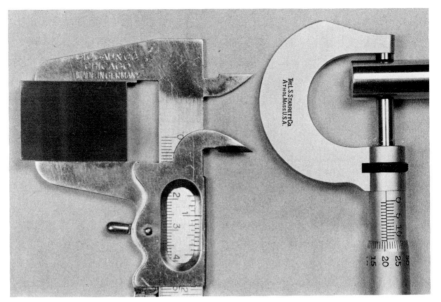

(Westinghouse Research and Development Center)

The Vernier Caliper (bottom), measuring a block of steel, shows both English (upper) and metric (lower) scales. On the metric scale, the match is between the fourth and fifth line, so the dimension is read 2.545 cm, equivalent to 1.00 inches on the inch scale. The micrometer caliper (top) has a metric scale, with the fixed scale marked in millimeters. The outer cylinder has 50 divisions around its circumference. One rotation of this outer cylinder moves the inner rod one-half millimeter. A diameter of 12.709 mm is being measured.

fixed scale, this means that the vernier scale has moved three-tenths of the distance between two marks on the fixed scale. Thus, if the fixed scale is marked in tenths of inches, the vernier reads hundredths of inches.

An extension of this device is the micrometer screw, which essentially stretches the scale by using a finely pitched thread. A large rotational movement is needed to produce a small linear movement. A suitably marked scale on the cylinder of the micrometer allows the linear distance to be measured with high precision. One revolution of the screw advances the pointer the distance determined by the pitch of the thread. A vernier scale is used to interpolate the distance covered by one complete revolution. With such a device it is possible to determine dimensions to 0.0001 inches (.00025 cm). Some instruments employ magnifying glasses to expand the scales, making it possible to determine dimensions to 0.00005 cm, which is 5,000 angstroms, or approximately the wavelength of visible light.

The most precise measurements use light beams. Since light has the property of waves, two light beams may be used to produce interference. This results in alternate addition and subtraction of the intensity of the two beams, which produces a series of light and dark bands visible through a suitable eyepiece or on a photographic plate.

One of the most extensive uses of this phenomenon is found in the interferometer, illustrated in Fig. 12.1, developed by Michelson. Monochromatic light from the sources travels to the mirror M which has a half-silvered surface. Such a surface has just enough silver to reflect half the light and transmit half. The reflected light proceeds to the mirror M_2 and the transmitted light goes to mirror M_1. These two mirrors are fully reflecting, and the two reflected beams again pass through mirror M and reach the telescope T as two parallel rays from

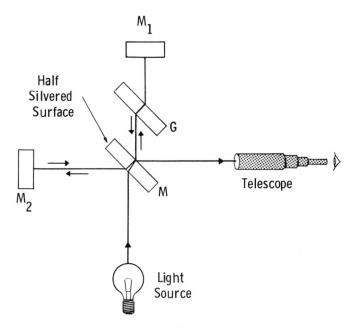

Michelson Interferometer

Figure 12.1

(Courtesy of Radio Corporation of America)

Electron microscope, an instrument that is finding widespread use in physical, biological, and medical research. Such instruments can give magnification up to 200,000 times and resolve dimensions as small as 10^{-7} cm.

(Westinghouse Research and Development Center)

Not grass, but iron oxide crystals growing from an iron wire. Photograph (A) was obtained by using an electron microscope with a magnification of 9,000; photograph (B) is the result of a magnification of 22,500.

135

a single source, which have traversed different paths. G is a compensating block, with the same dimensions as M. Thus, both light beams pass through glass of the same thickness. When the mirrors are properly adjusted, a series of dark and light bands are seen in the field of view of the telescope. If either M_1 or M_2 is moved in or out, the bands travel one way or the other across the field of view. When one of the mirrors is moved a distance equal to one-half a wavelength of the light used, the bands move a distance equal to that between the centers of two adjacent light bands. Thus, lengths may be determined to one-half the wavelength of light, or about 2×10^{-5} cm.

The smallest dimensions are observed with the aid of microscopes. In modern electron microscopes, narrow electron beams, with sufficient energy to affect photographic plates, are used instead of light rays. The lenses are magnetic instead of glass. With such devices as light microscopes and electron microscopes, man has been able to explore and measure objects of the microscopic world. He has at his disposal such high resolving power that he can observe details in viruses, which are little more than large molecules.

Electron microscopes can resolve dimensions as small as 6 angstroms, and plans are now underway to build one using a new development in superconductivity, with which strong magnetic fields can be obtained in small coils. With this device, it is hoped that dimensions as small as 2 angstroms can be resolved. We are coming closer and closer to the day when we will be able to "see" individual atoms.

The sense of time is very difficult to define, although it is one we all have. However, like all other natural senses, it is not capable of quantitative measurement, since to a large extent this sense is psychological in nature. For example, we have all experienced occasions when time "passed rapidly," while on other occasions time seemed to "drag very slowly." Time is the general term for the experience of duration. Like mass, space, and linear dimension, it is a fundamental concept. Duration—even the act of existence—presupposes a lapse of time, and therefore some means for its detection. Possibly lapse of time is based on the fact of repetition of experience. As discussed earlier, the repetition of sunrise and sunset, day and night, formed the first basis of time measurements. The sense of passage of time is too subjective for us to be very accurate in evaluating its duration without some external

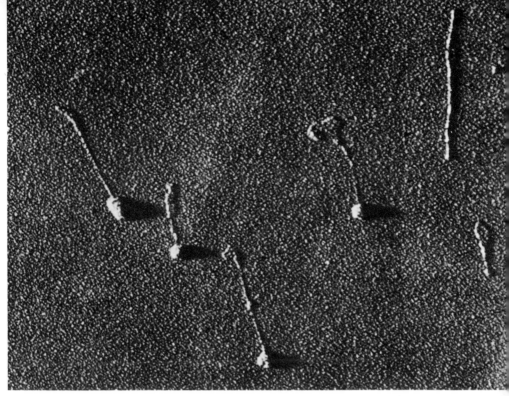

(Courtesy of E. C. Maclean (Miss) and C. E. Hall, Massachusetts Institute of Technology)
This photograph, taken with an electron microscope, shows bacteriophage (roundish objects) extruding DNA molecules. Magnification is 130,000 times.

standard. However, it is possible to estimate a second with reasonable accuracy by feeling our own pulse, which is slightly faster than one beat per second. Of course, the rate varies with varying circumstances; it can be almost doubled with strenuous exercise, or fear, or excitement, so the pulse rate is not a very reliable standard. With some practice, however, it is possible to learn to estimate the passage of time with a fair degree of accuracy by counting the pulse.

The most common instrument for measuring time, and certainly a far less subjective one, is the clock. With a good stop watch, it is possible to time events to a tenth of a second. One very accurate clock uses a crystal oscillator, similar to that described in our discussion of ultrasonics. Quartz crystals can be made to vibrate, if excited by an alternating electric field of the proper frequency. A thin quartz crystal is placed in the driving circuit of an oscillator, the characteristic of which is then determined by the dimensions of the crystal. With suitable cutting, the crystal's natural vibration frequency can be made insensi-

137

tive to temperature changes. Such crystal oscillators can be controlled with extreme precision, and will maintain a constant frequency to one part in 10^8 at a few megacycles over a period of a day. This corresponds to a time interval constant of about 10^{-9} seconds, or a millimicrosecond; with such devices it is possible to measure time intervals this small. Since modern research often involves this short an interval of time, it has been proposed that 10^{-9} seconds be adopted as a unit of time, called a *nanosecond.*

All clocks are subject to inaccuracies due to changes in temperature, humidity, or location, which result in changes in the gravitational force. For a long time scientists have dreamed of developing a clock that would not have this drawback. In 1954, they came a step closer to realizing their dream, when they invented a clock based on the vibration of ammonia molecules.

A stream of molecules is set to vibrating in an excited state, and allowed to pass into a microwave cavity, a metallic box excited to vibrate by high frequency radio waves. This microwave cavity is chosen to oscillate at the same frequency as the vibrational frequency of the excited ammonia molecules. When the ammonia beam enters the cavity, some of the molecules interact with the electric field produced by the microwaves and give up their vibrational energy to the cavity. This energy is then used to amplify the microwave signal. By suitable adjustments between the ammonia beam and the microwave signal, the cavity can be made to resonate with the same frequency as the vibration of the ammonia molecules. Such a clock is called a MASER, a term derived from the first letters of *Microwave Amplification by Stimulated Emission of Radiation,* which was the title of the scientific paper presented in 1951 by C. H. Townes, the physicist who discovered this effect.

The National Bureau of Standards, in Washington, D. C., has a clock based on this principle, using cesium atoms. It is so accurate that it will gain or lose only one second in 300 years, which corresponds to an accuracy of about one part in 10^{10}.

Change and Control

13

IN SENSING various observables, most of the detection involves sensing change in environment. For example, we are usually concerned with changes in light intensity, color, temperature, position, sound intensity, physical dimensions, and so on. We find ourselves in a constantly changing environment. All changes, however, can be expressed as changes in the four fundamental units of mass, length, time, and temperature. In most instances, our ability to sense changes, and hence to make measurements, depends on how well we can separate the events we are observing from spurious phenomena, which may be the result of uncontrolled changes in the experimental environment, including changes in the human observer, as we mentioned in a previous section. Measurements are meaningful *only* to the extent that the scientist can separate the controlled event from the uncontrolled events.

In many cases, scientists have learned to correlate changes in one observable with those in another. For example, it is possible to measure the change in temperature of an incandescent body by observing the change in color. Instruments called *pyrometers* are based on this principle, and are used for measuring the temperature of hot bodies. On the other hand, changes in temperature may also be determined by changes in the physical dimensions of an object or of a volume of fluid or gas.

Changes in velocity, length per unit time, may be determined in some cases by the change in frequency of sound or light radiating from the object. A train whistle changes pitch as it passes the observer. A bullet changes sound as it ricochets and changes velocity or direction. Such an effect is known as the *Doppler effect*. The frequency of sound or light waves, radiating from a moving object, increases in the direction of motion, and decreases in the direction opposite to the motion. This effect is given by the equation

$$n_1 = n\left(1 \pm \frac{v}{V}\right),$$

where n_1 is the frequency received, n the frequency of the source, V the velocity of sound or light, whichever the case in question, and v the velocity of the source.

Astronomers use the Doppler shift of light coming from the stars to determine the velocities of the stars in relation to the earth. This is only one of many examples.

The detection of change is involved in most measurements and presents the scientist with many difficult problems, because any physical measurement usually includes more than one observable. For example, a careful measurement of the length of an object must be made at constant temperature, since changes in temperature influence the dimensions. If a detector, such as a photomultiplier, is set to determine radiation from an event to be observed, it may be necessary to shield the multiplier from stray radiation which may be in the vicinity. In other words, careful experiments require carefully controlled conditions. The scientist must ascertain that the effect he observes is due only to a specific cause and is not a spurious effect, resulting from a change in some other condition. In many instances, it is necessary to go to extreme efforts to produce the required controlled conditions. For example, suppose a scientist wishes to study the reflection of electrons from a clean metallic surface. How can he do this? It is not enough to use ordinary cleaning procedures, because the surface is composed of an adsorbed gas layer, which will certainly influence the results. It is necessary, therefore, to prepare the surface in a vacuum, and this may be accomplished either by evaporating the metal film in the vacuum chamber, or by heating the surface to such a high temperature (about 2,000°C) that all the adsorbed gas is released, leaving a clean metallic surface.

If significant measurements are to be made, the vacuum must be extremely high to allow measuring before the molecules, present even in a good vacuum, can adsorb on the surface and form a film. For example, at atmospheric pressure and room temperature, there are

140

(Westinghouse Research and Development Center)
Vacuum environmental chamber. An ultrahigh vacuum system capable of producing pressures less than 10^{-12} atmospheres, used for the preparation of photosensitive surfaces for imaging tubes. Surfaces are poisoned by gas adsorption and must be prepared in an ultrahigh vacuum environment. Manipulations allow surfaces to be processed and assembled into the detector tubes while in the vacuum chamber.

about 4×10^{23} molecules striking every square centimeter of area every second. If we assume the diameter of a molecule, such as oxygen, to be 1×10^{-7} centimeters, and assume that we can treat the molecules as spheres, we can place 10^{14} spheres on a surface one centimeter square. We can then say that there are 10^{14} molecules per square centimeter in a monomolecular layer, such as the oxide film, on the surface of an object. Therefore, if we assume that, on an average, one molecule in four that strike the surface will stick; then, at atmospheric pressure, a monomolecular layer will form in 10^{-9} seconds.

The necessity for a good vacuum is obvious. At a pressure of 10^{-6} mm of mercury, 10^{14} molecules/sec will stick to the surface, and the monolayer will form in one second. At 10^{-9} mm of mercury, the layer will form in 1,000 seconds. This is long enough to perform measurements of reflectivity with good precision.

It takes considerable precaution and technical knowledge, however, to produce a vacuum of 10^{-9} mm of Hg, or less. Ultrahigh vacuum techniques, recently developed, allow such vacuums to be achieved

(Courtesy of General Electric Space Technology Center)

Part of the large Space Environment Facility of the General Electric Space Technology Center. The huge dome rolls into place, sealing the vacuum chamber; giant diffusion pumps evacuate this chamber to pressures as low as 10^{-12} atmospheres. Baffles, cooled by liquid helium, simulate the extreme cold of outer space, and various radiation sources may be used to simulate the radiation effects found in space.

142

with reasonable care. But this means that the scientist must now have a knowledge of ultrahigh vacuum techniques in order to produce an environment in which he can control the conditions of his experiment. Depending on the nature of his measurements, he may also find it necessary to control the temperature of the environment, and in addition, he may have to shield his detectors from spurious electromagnetic radiation.

Another example of environment control is illustrated in the photoconductors discussed earlier. We mentioned that if we wish to detect infrared radiation, which is a form of heat energy, the thermal radiation from the surroundings may produce such a background noise that the signal is swamped. In this case, the detector may be placed in a cryostat (a low-temperature refrigerator) and cooled to liquid-helium temperatures, which can be held constant at the low value of 4° Kelvin. This greatly reduces the background noise of thermal radiation, and makes it possible to detect the infrared signal. The development of technology

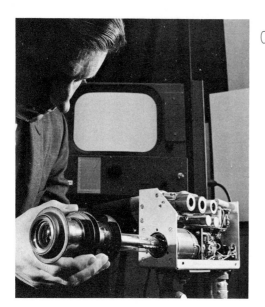 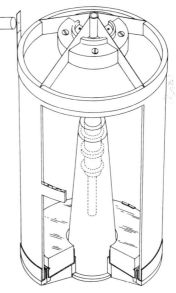

(Westinghouse Research and Development Center)

Ultraviolet sensor, a new telescope which senses ultraviolet radiation. The radiation produces electrons which are converted by electronic circuits into radio waves. Fired into space on rockets and satellites, these sensors detect ultraviolet radiation in space and this information is telemetered to earth as radio waves.

143

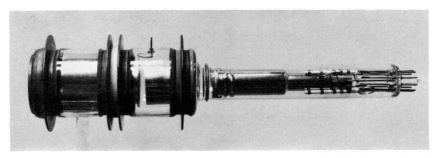

(Westinghouse Research and Development Center)

Ultraviolet sensor tube for space. Ultraviolet light is converted by electrons into video signals. This tube will be used in an orbiting astronomical telescope.

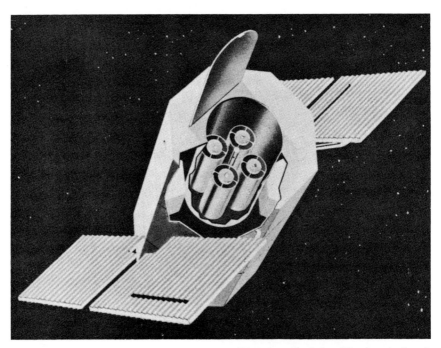

(Westinghouse Research and Development Center)

Artist's conception of the orbiting astronomical observatory. The four cylinders are four separate telescopes; mirrors at the bottom focus an image on the surface of the sensor tube shown in the preceding photograph. Starlight intensities in the range of 1,000 Å to 3,000 Å will be measured and telemetered to earth. Large vanes contain solar cells for converting radiation into electrical power to operate the sensor tube and telemetering system.

144

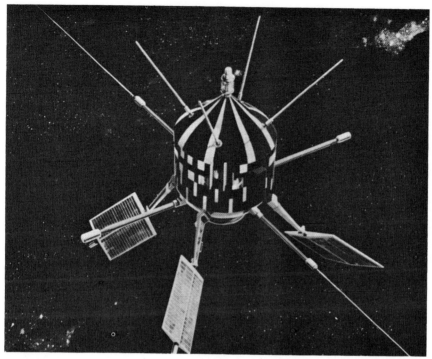

(Westinghouse Electric Corporation, Air Arm Division)

Artist's conception of the UK-2/S-52 Satellite. An orbiting scientific satellite jointly designed by scientists of the United States and the United Kingdom to detect (1) galactic noise (radiation sensing), (2) atmospheric ozone (by radiation absorption), (3) micrometeoroid flux (micrometeoroids pierce holes in a thin foil, light shining through holes is detected by radiation sensors, and counted).

and apparatus for working with liquid helium requires a good deal of specialized training, and in order to conduct his experiments, the scientist may find it necessary to learn cryogenic or low-temperature techniques.

These are only two of countless examples of the importance in scientific investigation of being able to control the environment, or being able to create the proper one in which to perform experiments.

As man strives to master his environment, he is continually sensing, measuring, and interpreting. Each interpretation then forms the basis for new sensings, new measurements, and new interpretations. These probings into the nature of his surroundings may be observations of

145

the interplay of atoms, or observations of galaxies. They may be relatively inexpensive, routine, unspectacular measurements by a single person; or they may involve millions of dollars, expenditures that demand the trained efforts of hundreds of scientists, such as those required for a space satellite probe. Whatever the experiment, the scientist, as he always has, is continually bumping into the barrier called the limit of detection. It is this limit which always has and always will furnish the motivation for devising ingenious new methods of extending the range of our natural senses.

Limits of Observation

The Nature of Noise

14

FEW DREAMS have so haunted man as that of extending the limits of his senses. To see the farthest stars, to watch the smallest microcosm, to feel the slightest force, to hear sounds produced far away or long ago; these aspirations required only the extension of human powers for their realization. To this end he built telescopes and microscopes, microbalances, telephones, radio tubes, and recorders. But he also longed to understand the world around him, and he created in his mind—at first tentatively—an image of nature's mechanism, then tested the reality of this image by experimentation. This, too, required the extension of human senses, but in new dimensions that called for qualitative rather than quantitative changes. It meant sensing physical variables concealed from direct perception, such as voltage and current, magnetic fields or x rays; it also meant measuring these quantities, that is, comparing their size with basic units as accurately as possible. The instruments needed for these purposes convert the physical variable, the signal, into a visible or audible indication, which can then be compared with a calibrated scale. This, of course, is measurement. All the principles on which these direct or indirect extensions of the human senses are based can be refined, magnified, and stretched to achieve greater and greater sensing powers, and it often appears that such improvements can be endless.

It is true that the process of amplifying a current or a voltage, for example, can be repeated almost arbitrarily, often by the simple expedient of cascading a sufficient number of amplifying stages. Thus, the original signal, produced by light or sound in the photosurface or microphone of the pickup devices in a distant television station, may have to undergo a cumulative amplification by a factor of 10^{15} before it is reproduced with sufficient contrast and volume by the receiver in our living room. Occasionally, we may be uncomfortably aware of noise that has been introduced at some stage, but it is also characteristic of such disturbances that they can be remedied by simple measures, such as introducing yet another amplification stage somewhere in the chain.

However, deeply rooted in the nature of the detection process there are disturbances generally called fundamental noise, although they affect signals other than sound. These perturbations limit measurement or observation in a manner that, in principle, cannot be remedied by amplification or magnification. It is important to understand this distinction: just as the most perfect and powerful radio receiver cannot correct the grammatical mistakes of a radio announcer, no amount of amplification or magnification can reduce the fundamental noise. It is easy to see that these limitations are of interest in their own right. Not only do they tell us to what extent information can be gained— or rather saved—by adding amplification stages, but their very existence may reveal aspects of nature which had been undetected by any other approach. Hence, it is sometimes more important to study the noise than the signal. But these arguments are speculative and academic so far; we will fortify them with examples of experiments which are easy to follow in thought, if not in fact.

Suppose we were to try to investigate the sounds made by insects, the pitch, the modulation, and perhaps the meaning as messages from one individual to another. The sounds of larger organisms, such as bees and crickets, obviously present no serious problem of measuring and recording; available microphones are sensitive enough for the level of sound produced by these insects, at least at close range. But the situation is different when we are dealing with smaller or perhaps microscopic creatures; the whir of a fruit fly's wings must exist, although it is inaudible to the most sensitive human ear, and there may or may not be such emanation from all that crawls, hops, or flies. To study this tiny world of sound we would have to construct extremely delicate instruments especially for the purpose. A suitable ultramicrophone would have to be equipped with a membrane which is small and light enough to respond to the minute changes in air pressure produced by such a source of sound. With modern laboratory methods it is in fact possible to prepare membranes only a few molecules thick. If such a

(Westinghouse Research and Development Center)

The free film of aluminum oxide shown here, about 200 angstroms (2×10^{-6} cm) thick, is the oxide layer of household aluminum foil freed from the metal by chemical means. Although a layer only about 25 molecules in thickness, this film is relatively strong, as demonstrated by its supporting the weight of a spider. The thinness of such sensitive films illustrates how the construction of certain sensing devices may involve going to the possible limit to achieve response to the smallest detectable signals.

thin free film is made metallically conducting (by the choice of a proper material or the evaporation of metal atoms onto it) and positioned at a small distance in front of a metal plate, a capacitive microphone results. When a sound wave imposes slight changes on the spacing, an electric charge on the membrane will produce corresponding voltage pulses, and these can be amplified to any extent, and displayed or recorded. (See Fig. 14.1.) It would seem that the system could be made to work with almost unlimited sensitivity by proper construction of the capacitor and the amplifier, making it possible, for example, to hear the sound of moths "chewing the rag." Unfortunately, as the microphone is made more and more sensitive, a limit is reached: depending

151

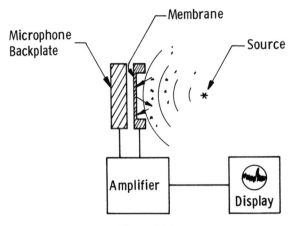

Figure 14.1

on the bandwidth of the amplifier, a hissing or crackling sound becomes audible. This disturbance goes on even in the absence of any specimen or other visible source, drowning out all other sound that is smaller; no improvement in construction or increase of amplification can eliminate it. We are encountering, in fact, the din of individual air molecules as they strike and pummel the membrane. The very medium which carries the sound also carries its own noise, and no device can circumvent or subtract this inherent disorder.

Thus we are dealing with what might be called a fundamental noise limitation. We already know two salient facts about its cause and nature: its existence is related, first, to the fact that the medium of sound propagation consists not of a continuum, but of discrete particles called molecules; and second, to the fact that these molecules are in constant irregular motion, so that their arrival on the membrane is completely random. If this were not the case, and the air molecules impinged on the membrane at regular intervals, we could effectively subtract or cancel the disturbance, since its occurrence would be predictable. Actually, the human senses have such a built-in sense of abstraction; the eye, for instance, is able to distinguish forms and marks, even at low contrast, against a regular pattern like ruled paper. Thus, if we encounter periodic or otherwise predictable disturbances, we speak of "background" rather than of noise. However, noise is characterized by the irregularity or unpredictability of its occurrence.

Nevertheless, even for fundamental limitations there is one method of improving the signal-to-noise ratio, or the ratio of the stimulus from the source to be measured to the stimulus caused by disorder. So far, in the microphone example, we have tacitly assumed that the apparatus is capable of reproducing any sound, regardless of its frequency or pitch. Sound audible to the human ear covers a frequency range of about 15 to 15,000 cycles per second. On the other hand, it is possible to limit the range of signals passed by the amplifier (the *band pass* or *bandwidth*) to a much smaller region, say a few cycles. The system will then be sensitive to the "tuned" frequency with a relatively high signal-to-noise ratio, since it rejects all but the noise containing vibrations in the admitted frequency interval. In exchange, there is a price to pay: the limitation to a narrow frequency interval increases proportionately the time needed for observation. It will be explained later, in the discussion of shot noise in *More and More Noise* of Part Four, that there is the following approximate relationship:

$$\tau \cong \frac{1}{2\Delta f},$$

where τ is the time any resonant system needs to respond with a sharpness (or bandwidth) Δf.

This equation implies that a bandwidth of one cycle per second (for instance, a band pass between 10,000 and 10,001 cycles per second) necessitates an observation time of one second by order of magnitude. By the same rule, if one admits only a change of one cycle every 100 seconds ($\Delta f = 0.01 \text{ sec}^{-1}$), it obviously requires an observation time in the order of 100 seconds to notice a change in amplitude or phase. Thus we find that by limiting our "listening range," that is by admitting a limited frequency interval, we reject the noise in other frequencies but also extend the listening time needed.

This relationship between length of observation and signal-to-noise ratio can be demonstrated in a somewhat different manner. Suppose we want to evaluate the frequency spectrum of some source of sound, say that of a whistle. We mean by this that we undertake measuring the amplitude of sound as a function of pitch. This type of experiment is conveniently performed with a cathode ray oscilloscope; the horizontal deflection (abscissa) is a measure of frequency; the vertical deflection (ordinate) represents the sound volume. A single sweep between a lower and upper limit of frequency already outlines the frequency spectrum, albeit with a certain amount of "jitter" due to noise. Now suppose we "integrate" over many sweeps, that is, we measure both signal and noise cumulatively by taking periodic readings over the total spectrum, and add up the readings for each frequency. (See Fig. 14.2.) We will then find that the noise integrated over a certain length of time is proportional to the square root of such time, whereas the signal accumulates linearly with it. It follows that the signal-to-noise ratio increases with the square root of the observation time. (Related behavior of the variance σ_m is discussed in Chapter Seven, "Some Figures.") This is shown in Fig. 14.2, where subsequent cumulative readings start with a signal at frequency f_0, while the latter is competing with random noise in the surrounding spectrum at a ratio of about $1:1$. It is apparent that if the subsequent responses are allowed to accumulate, the signal emerges victorious in proportion to the square root of the elapsed time.

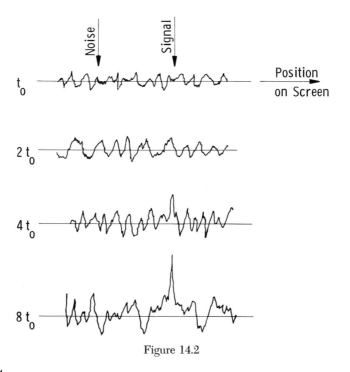

Figure 14.2

Counting

15

WE HAVE discussed the ultramicrophone at such length not because the measurement of minute sound energies is of primary importance, but because the limitations we have mentioned, although easily understood on the basis of the kinetic theory of gases, are actually representative of a much wider and deeper-rooted class of principles that govern atomic physics. First we must realize that we can deal in *thought* with concepts of time, length, and mass as continuous and therefore divisible and subdivisible to an unlimited extent, but in *fact* we are confronted by nature with measurable quantities of more or less coarse graininess. By this we mean that anything we use for or subject to measurement is of atomistic structure, consisting of discrete entities. Electric charges can thus occur only as a multiplicity of electrons, and when we measure a current, in effect we count the number of electrons passing each second through a plane. We encounter no different situation in determining the density of a substance, since this amounts to counting atoms or molecules. Even energy, which to all appearances is a smooth function of such variables as height, turns out to be "quantized," aside from being measurable only by atomistic tools. Of course, discreteness of energy, for instance, in units of *photons* for light and of *phonons* for sound or of *magnetons* for the magnetic moments of atoms, was last to be discovered, most resistant to intuitive understanding, and most difficult to generalize for all forms. Furthermore, the atomistic structure of mass, charge, and energy had been undetected for so long because of the enormous number of individual entities needed to make up macroscopic amounts. An ampere-second or coulomb consists of 6.25×10^{18} electrons, a gram of iron of 1.08×10^{22} atoms, and a watt-second or joule of radiant energy—delivered, for instance, as green light—consists of 3×10^{18} photons. On a macroscopic scale, such graininess is therefore exceedingly fine, which turns out to be the result of evolution rather than of accident. Indeed, it is mainly when we pursue the process of detection or measurement to its limits that we come to grips with the finiteness of the numbers with which we are dealing.

Fluctuations

16

SUPPOSE we try to count the number of raindrops falling per minute in a steady downpour on areas of a given size, such as panes of glass. This example represents the counting of *random events* whose occurrence is quite unpredictable. The counts we perform minute by minute for each pane will fluctuate; in general, some counts will be the same or nearly the same, others will be higher or lower. In other words, the counts follow some form of distribution. The most probable kind of distribution will depend on such physical conditions as whether the raindrops tend to clump together, or effectively repel each other.

However, we will assume two ideal conditions, which in fact we are entitled to do in the case of raindrops and many other physical situations. First, the events are entirely independent of each other; that is, the arrival of one raindrop does not in any way hasten or delay the arrival of any other. Second, the physical conditions do not change during observation; the gross rate of arrival remains constant. We will say, then, the randomness is complete. Thus, since there are no restrictions on the time and place of their arrival, all drops could have come down at the same point, or their arrival time could have been spaced at certain intervals, producing the noise, say, of a lively polka. Either of these distributions are admissible, but they are extremely unlikely. In fact, it is easy to see that the arrival frequency is likely to fluctuate around a mean or average value. Under the conditions cited, the most probable distribution is given by the *Poisson Law*. But here we are concerned with only one aspect of the Poisson distribution: the expected deviation from the mean. Obviously, this will represent the uncertainty with which a fluctuating quantity can be measured.

If we divide the total number N of raindrops by the area and the time of observation and counting, we obtain the average number

$\langle n \rangle_{av}$ of raindrops falling on unit area per unit time. The suggested experiment of actually counting the drops falling on individual panes (unit squares) each minute will yield certain numbers, n_1 for the first square, n_2 for the second, and so on. The average of these is also $\langle n \rangle_{av}$. We can now define certain deviations from the mean:

$$\Delta n_1 = n_1 - \langle n \rangle_{av}; \; \Delta n_2 = n_2 - \langle n \rangle_{av}; \; \Delta n_3 = n_3 - \langle n \rangle_{av} \ldots .$$

The sum of all these deviations must be zero because there are, by definition, as many counts above the average as there are below it. Therefore, the mean value of the deviations is also zero. However, we always obtain positive values for the square of the deviations $\Delta n_i^2 = (n_i - \langle n \rangle)^2$ and their average $\langle (\Delta n_i)^2 \rangle_{av}$. This is called "mean square deviation" or "variance," and we will find that an important relation holds true with an accuracy that improves with greater numbers $\langle n \rangle$, as follows:

$$\langle (\Delta n)^2 \rangle_{av} = \langle n \rangle \quad \text{or} \quad \Delta n_{rms} = \sqrt{n},$$

where we have omitted the symbols for averages. In other words, the square of the deviations from the mean can be expected to be about equal to the mean. Thus, if we find that on the average 100 drops fall per minute on a glass pane, the mean square deviation is also about 100. The deviations themselves are about equal to the square root of the mean, in this case on the order of plus or minus 10. If we count 12 squares, we may find, for instance, the following scatter of counts:

103, 111, 91, 95, 100, 89, 108, 109, 102, 97, 88, 112.

If the average n were 1,000, the actual counts would fluctuate by about $\sqrt{1,000} \cong 32$, that is, between about 970 and 1,030. This law is quite general, and is valid for all counts of random events; the accuracy improves as the numbers themselves become larger and larger.

About the best example of the relationship between randomness and fluctuations is furnished by the phenomenon of radioactivity. The fluctuations governing radioactive processes can be conveniently demonstrated with luminous watch dials. The luminescence is usually produced by the admixture of very small amounts of radium to the bulk of some phosphor, such as zinc sulfide, which makes up the dial markings. As individual radium atoms decay, they emit energetic

158

particles, and it is this bombardment of the phosphor which creates light visible to the dark-adapted eye. Now, the experiment we suggest is very simple: Some night when sleep is evasive anyway, hold a luminous watch close to one eye; at a distance of about a quarter of an inch from the glass, the pupil is filled with phosphorescent light. (To avoid radiation danger, it is better to observe the phosphor through a magnifying glass.) It will then be found that the luminescence is not continuous, but fluctuates; in fact, the eye detects scintillations resulting from individual atomic events.

The connection to randomness is this: Any given radium atom has a life expectancy of about 1,600 years. Obviously, it would be a very unprofitable undertaking to select a few atoms and wait until they die with the emission of an alpha-particle and transition to a new type of atom. Not the least consideration is that the individual life expectancy is entirely independent of the time the atom has already been in existence. After 20,000 years, a surviving atom is still as good as new. The prognosis is for another 1,600 years but, alas, it may decay before our eyes within the next hour, without any external cause. The physical surroundings and conditions may be identical; yet the lifetime is random.

Nevertheless, the concept of a definite lifetime has a particular meaning if it is applied to a large number of individuals. In the case of radium, we find that half of any quantity that is large enough to be weighed will have decayed in exactly 1,620 years. In other words, a highly predictable radioactive behavior is found when radium, or any of its salts such as radium sulfate, is measured in micrograms or milligrams which contain, respectively, 10^{15} and 10^{18} of its atoms. A half-life of centuries or more can be only indirectly determined, of course. The decay product of radium is an inert gas, radon (or radium emanation), which is quite easily separated and volumetrically evaluated. Thus, we find that a salt containing 10^{20} radium atoms produces per day 4.35×10^{-6} cc of radon at normal pressure and temperature, and this amounts to 1.17×10^{14} atoms of the gas. From this data for radium it is easy to compute the decay rate (1.36×10^{-11} per sec.) and half-life (1,620 years). The daughter substance, radon, is again radioactive; its half-life is 3.83 days. This is most easily determined by separating a certain amount of the gas and measuring the ebbing of its radioactivity with time. It is here that once more we encounter the mean square deviation law.

Suppose we start with 10^{14} radon atoms. These produce, in accordance with the stated lifetime, 2.09×10^8 disintegrations per second; however, not all of these are observable, and typically only 0.1 per cent of these events are caught by scintillation counting. Thus, on the average, an electronic counter would register 2.09×10^5 flashes each second. We emphasize that this is an average value; according to the fluctuation law, the square root of this number, ± 458, appears as a mean deviation, and were we to rely on the measurement taken during one second, the relative error (or accuracy) $\Delta N_{rms}/N$ would be 1/458, or about 0.2 per cent. Of course, if we extend the observation time to 100 seconds, the accuracy improves to 0.02 per cent, and so on. It does not matter if we perform a single observation during 100 seconds, or average 100 measurements of only one second's duration. In other words, the accuracy increases with the square root of the cumulative observation time, regardless of how this time is subdivided. However, for long observation times, we may have to correct for systematic changes of the measured value. All these considerations enter an actual determination of the radon half-life, for we find, within the limits of accuracy described, that the radon count rate is reduced by a factor of 2 every 3.83 days. Thus, the frequency of flashes in our example of $2.09 \times 10^5 \ \text{sec}^{-1}$ is reduced by $2^5 = 32$ after $5 \times 3.83 = 19$ days, and by $2^{10} = 1,024$ after 38 days, at which time the count rate will be 204 ± 14 per second.

Finally, after about two months, radioactivity of the gaseous material has almost ceased with a scintillation appearing only in erratic intervals of a few seconds. The radioactive events, incidentally, are not yet completed; solid deposits are formed in the disintegration of the emanation (called consecutively, Radium A, B, C, . . . F, in the order in which they are created) until at last a stable element, lead, is formed.

Of course, we could cite many more examples for the fluctuation in the number of random events. The generalization is obvious, and in combination with the example given previously in Chapter 15, "Counting," it adds up to an interesting conclusion regarding the statistical nature of measurement. For at this point we can fuse these two distinctly different elements of the process of measurement:

160

All sensing, detecting, and observing deals with atomistic matter, whether it be energy, charge, or mass. Therefore, the quantitative aspect of these processes, in other words, the measuring, amounts to counting discrete entities, whether they are quanta, electrons, or atoms.

If these atomistic entities are randomly distributed in time or space, their number will fluctuate when counted under otherwise equal conditions.

Now it follows from these two statements that an inherent uncertainty, which we may call noise or error, attaches itself to any measurement that deals with randomized particles. On first reflection, it will seem that randomness is encountered as the exception rather than the rule. In fact, as the examples of raindrops and radioactive disintegrations show, the very essence of randomness is freedom in the choice of variables; in other words, the absence of restraints and restrictions that would prevent a particle from arriving at any arbitrary time or position. But we know that atoms, electrons, and so on, are very much under restraint as a rule in that they are bound to certain locations; indeed, this is the most important prerequisite for the existence of the solid state. It would appear, then, that we could avoid all fluctuations and the tiresome disturbances that they entail, merely by employing media for our measurements in which individual corpuscles are under rigid constraints, like the atoms of a crystal as hard as diamond.

The difficulty with this idea of avoiding randomness by enforcing rigid restraints is that it can not, as a matter of principle, be reconciled with the process of measurement. For example, suppose we want to measure the volume of an irregularly shaped container. Of course, the classical method is to fill the volume with water, and then measure the amount in a calibrated cylinder. There are variations of this technique, and while they may be capable of greater refinement, all amount to occupying the volume with a medium which can adapt itself smoothly to the contours of the container and thus fill it uniformly. That this demands certain freedom of motion for the atoms of the medium, rather than rigidity, goes without saying. To use a high-viscosity fluid, such as honey or tar, would strike us as no more suitable for the purpose than using marbles. Sand, however, whose flow is still used as a crude measure of time, could also be applied as a gauge for volume. Clearly, the finer the sand the better it performs this task; if we think this process of refinement through to the limit, we arrive finally at the atoms of a liquid with low viscosity. Thus, we are led back to the necessity of allowing freedom of motion for the atomistic particles of the medium; to be able to measure at all, we have to take into the bargain the attending randomness of individual events and the fluctuations of the ensemble.

All this means that every measurement is of statistical nature; not just the measurement concerned with the number of individuals exercising free choice of one or the other alternative, or the measurement of biological occurrences, but the physical measurement of nature's universally and eternally constant values, about whose permanence we would expect to entertain no doubt. To summarize our conclusions, we have found that

(1) The objects and tools of measurement are atomistic.
(2) Therefore, all measurement amounts to counting individual entities.
(3) To be useful for measurement, these particles must be allotted certain freedoms of motion at the price of a commensurate randomness.
(4) The occurrence of random events is accompanied by fluctuations in their numbers for given intervals of time and space.
(5) Therefore, all measurement is unavoidably perturbed by fluctuations, and these are evaluated as noise.

Indeed, were it not for this fundamental flaw of our universe in exhibiting atomistic structure, even the smallest signals would be detectable, and there would be no limit to the accuracy with which anything could be measured. Nor would there be, from the physicist's point of view, much of anything worth measuring.

More and More Noise

17

Fundamental Noise

WE ARE now ready to tackle an important problem in the science of measurement—evaluating the limits set by noise. Actually, in the development of physics over the last century, these limits were recognized one by one, and the various noise sources were named for their discoverers as well as for the individual effects. This means that different names can refer to identical phenomena. With the perfect vision of hindsight, however, most noise powers can be derived on the basis of the same principles.

In view of the previous discussion, it should not be too difficult to guess the method of procedure. We first establish the relationship of conventional units, such as units of current or heat content, to their basic atomistic entities, such as electronic charge and the equipartition unit of heat, the kT explained in Chapter 9, "Sensing Pressure and Sound." This is a relatively simple process which tells us with little calculation how many particles we will find, on the average, in a given signal for a given time of observation. The second step is to compute the fluctuation of this number according to the law of mean deviation. The third step is to convert this number back into practical units, and this is the answer we want, of course, since it represents the noise.

Sometimes, the second step presents real difficulties when there is not complete randomness for the events counted, as we have assumed. Instead, there may be partial restrictions on the freedom of occurrence for the individual events, and this leads to a different "statistics," which in turn generates its own kind of fluctuation law. Rather than deplore this vexing complexity of nature, we may turn adversity to advantage

163

by exploring the noise itself. We can then test any theory we may have formed about the nature of randomness restrictions and the correctness of any statistics following from it.

Shot Noise

Perhaps the most important of the disturbances which plague those intent on delicate sensing, detecting, or measuring are associated with the observation of very small electric quantities. In particular, we will discuss the noise that occurs principally whenever we want to register a small current, or a small change of current, in response to a stimulant or signal. In a typical situation a stream of electrons emerges from a metal surface (cathode) and passes through a vacuum toward another metal surface (anode). (See Fig. 17.1.) This happens in phototubes where the incidence of light on a cathode of suitable material produces electrons in numbers that increase linearly with the radiation intensity. It is also characteristic of the thermionic current with which virtually all electron tubes are operated; indeed it is characteristic of the passage of any particle stream through or onto a barrier, regardless of the nature of the medium, whether it be from solid to vacuum, from vacuum to solid, or from solid to solid. Devices that employ electron barriers usually have the purpose of controlling current in order to detect or amplify a signal such as light on photocathodes, or a small voltage impressed on a grid that faces an emitter. These devices operate in somewhat

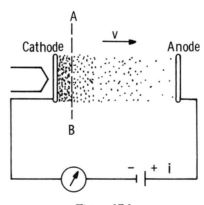

Figure 17.1

the same way as a faucet with a valve for controlling the flow of water. This comparison is not exactly novel, since the British call the electron tube a "valve." Our interest in the faucet concerns the valve when it is nearly closed and the flow of water is only a dribble, an irritating stutter of individual drops. Something similar, at least in appearance, happens when the current flow from the cathode is very small and the beam appears to become grainy. In contrast to the valve analogy, this graininess is always present in the electron structure. Such nearly expiring current, amplified and fed to a loudspeaker, generates a noise similar to the sound of lead pellets falling irregularly on a hard surface. Hence this effect is called *shot noise* (also, less ambiguously, Schottky noise, after its discoverer). The process is quite similar to the raindrop example for random events. How can the noise current be expressed in terms of these fluctuations? To answer this we proceed in three steps:

First, electric current i is defined as the amount of charge passing per second through a real or imaginary boundary; if we observe the current for a time t a charge $i \times t$ will have passed, and since such a charge is atomistic, consisting of n electrons of unit e, it follows that the number of electrons that pass through the barrier is

$$n = \frac{i \times t}{e} = \frac{i}{e \times 2\Delta f}.$$

On the right of this expression, we have replaced the observation time t by its reciprocal value, $t = 1/2\Delta f$, where Δf is the bandwidth, mentioned earlier. This name was originated in pioneering days of radio; it represents the width of frequencies the apparatus will admit around the tuned value (or more accurately, the frequency range between which the apparatus response is greater than 0.7 of its maximum value at resonance). The relationship between Δf and t is the same as that described in Chapter 14, "The Nature of Noise," except for a small factor which follows from a different meaning of "observation" time. Since Δf is the range of frequencies the system will accept, it follows that it will "tolerate" Δf changes in amplitude per second and, therefore, have a memory or observation time in the order of $1/\Delta f$. A somewhat involved mathematical treatment corrects this by a factor of ½ for the integration time of random noise.

As a second step, we decide that the emergence of electrons through the barrier is an unrestrained random process. Therefore, we apply the root-mean-square deviation law:

$$\langle(\Delta n)^2\rangle_{av} = \frac{\langle\Delta i^2\rangle_{av} \times t^2}{e^2} = n.$$

Finally, we interpret the fluctuations in the number of electrons and the corresponding fluctuation of the current i_n as noise, and obtain:

$$i_n{}^2 = 2ei\Delta f = 3.18 \times 10^{-19} \times i\Delta f,$$

which is the shot noise formula for a current i (in amperes). This relation is basic for the ultimate limitation of photoelectric sensors and thermionic current devices. It also applies to the random generation and recombination of charge carriers in semiconductors, and thus to photoconductors, transistors, and other solid-state devices. The limitation is best explained in terms of the ratio of the signal current i to the noise current i_n (the rms-value being understood):

$$\frac{i}{i_n} = \sqrt{\frac{i}{2e\Delta f}} = \sqrt{\frac{i}{3.18 \times 10^{-19}\Delta f}}.$$

Thus the signal-to-noise ratio increases directly as the square root of the current. For instance, at television bandwidths, $f = 4$ megacycles/sec, the signal-to-noise ratio is about unity for a current of 10^{-12} amperes. These considerations proved most important for the design of television pick-up devices and similar systems.

It is worth expanding this example of television camera tubes, because it illustrates clearly the nature of the limitations the fundamental noises impose on the performance of electronic devices. Unlike the apparently simultaneous evaluation of the human eye-brain system, the method of television consists of consecutive probing or *scanning*. An image is formed on a light-sensitive film, as it is on the eye retina, and this reacts by a process of photoemission or photoconduction according to the intensity distribution. In the case of photoemission, electrons focused on a second screen form a corresponding charge image; but these details are not important here. What interests us is that, whatever the mechanism, it involves a point-by-point probing of the sensitive film by an electron beam scanned over the area in a pattern of about 500 lines repeated 30 times a second. Obviously, such a process makes certain demands on the bandwidth and the beam current. The bandwidth is determined by the requirement that the system portray 200 to 300 picture elements per scanning line, 500 lines per frame, 30 frames per second; in other words, the carrier frequency is modulated by $500 \times 300 \times 30 = 4.5 \times 10^6$ changes per second, which defines the bandwidth. The bandwidth, in turn, affects the noise level of the probing current: the faster the beam races over the area, the fewer electrons are available for probing a given elemental picture area. Hence a fluctuation results, which competes with the signal resulting from a certain light level at the particular point. The formulas for shot noise, which we have discussed, help us decide the beam current needed for a desired signal-to-noise ratio, and similar considerations apply to the target behavior.

In semiconductors, a type of fluctuation occurs which is an interesting variation of shot noise. Semiconductors are actually very much like insulators, because they can carry current only when charges are generated throughout their bulk by an external source of energy. Such an energy source can simply be heat, and semiconductors are characterized by a conductivity which increases with temperature. Again, current carriers can also be produced by the energy of light, a phenomenon called photoconductivity. We mention in passing that the difference between semiconductors and insulators is mainly a matter of degree; in insulators greater energy is necessary for the production of carriers and hence the temperature needed for the onset of conduction will break the bonds between the ions of the solid, which may melt or otherwise disintegrate unless an ionic type of conductivity takes over.

The fluctuations in semiconductors arise from the random events of the birth and death of charge carriers. An important mechanism, for instance, is one in which there are *impurity centers* capable of donating, at the slightest provocation, an electron which can carry its share of current for a while, until, after a mean life τ it recombines with an empty impurity state, and thus disappears from circulation. Therefore, we have at any moment an *average* electron population composed of a number n of individuals per unit volume. But because of the random nature of generation and recombination, the actual count during an observation time t will fluctuate from one measure-

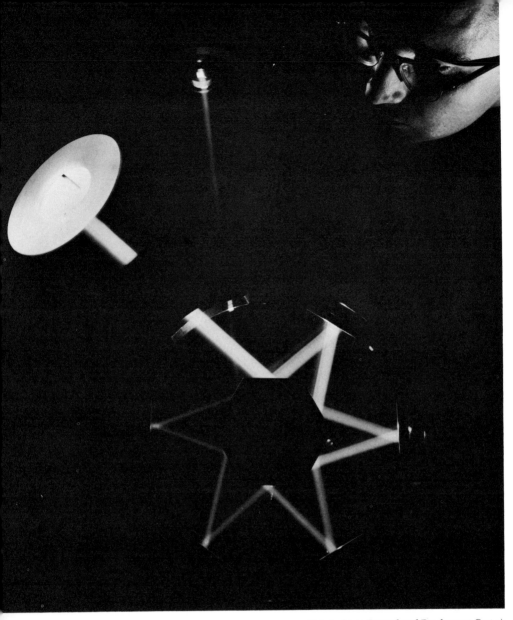

(Westinghouse Research and Development Center)

This "light chopper" mechanically generates light pulses of extremely short duration. The collimated beam from a light source is repeatedly reflected between a set of mirrors, some rotating and some stationary. This results in the star pattern, made visible here by tobacco smoke which also attenuates the beam. In actual operation the central hexagonal mirror spins at about 15,000 revolutions per minute, and attenuation due to reflection losses is quite small. The beam finally passes through a suitable aperture in pulses of 10^{-8} seconds duration. The device is used for such applications as the measurement of response time in radiation detectors. Its ultimate limitation is the sensitivity of the radiation detector. Thus the shortest measurable time (in the order of $10^{-9} = 10^{-10}$ seconds) is finally given by shot or generation-recombination noise.

ment to the next. Since the average lifetime is τ, we count t/τ generations of carriers per observation time, and all together we have:

$$N = nt/\tau = \frac{n}{2\tau\Delta f}$$

individual electrons on the average. The mean square of the noise voltage is then proportional to the reciprocal of this value. Thus, for the *generation-recombination* noise, we have:

$$V_{n,\,\mathrm{rms}} \propto \left(\frac{2\tau\Delta f}{n}\right)^{1/2}.$$

Since one man's noise is another man's signal, we can use this last relation to derive the lifetime of the carriers in the semiconductor from the *G-R* fluctuations at a known bandwidth.

Photon Noise

The radiation from sources of visible and invisible light, or even from radio antennas, consists of discrete entities, the *photons*. We have every right to expect a certain randomness in the individual emission process, and therefore it is not surprising that radiation itself is noisy.

Nevertheless, the fluctuation law is not exactly the same as in the cases we have discussed so far. If during a given time interval we count an average arrival contingent of N photons of sufficiently short wavelengths, in the visible or x-ray region, we still observe the usual $N^{1/2}$ rms-deviation. But as we repeat this experiment for longer wavelengths, the fluctuations systematically increase so that they assume several times the normal value in the far infrared and beyond.

The reason for this behavior has to be sought in the nature of the randomness with which photons are emitted. If we explore this phenomenon in greater detail, we find that individual emissions are not completely independent of each other. A process exists which is the exact opposite of absorption, one in which an incident photon encountering an excited state is not absorbed, but instead generates a second photon. This is called *stimulated emission* or *negative absorption*. The first photon creates the stimulated photon in its own image, so to speak, giving it the same frequency, the same timing or phase, and

169

even the same direction. We mention in passing that all this is fundamental to coherent radiation, especially to masers and lasers. For fluctuation theory, these radiation processes imply that photons emerging from a black body have a chance to be absorbed and then they are concealed from observation; those we do observe, however, have a finite chance of belonging to a pair, one stimulating and one stimulated photon. Thus we have a deviation from complete randomness since the arrival of a photon is not completely independent of the arrival of the next. This deviation from the normal fluctuation law generates the larger noise.

The situation is important to the designer of detecting equipment. He may carefully avoid any disturbances caused by contact graininess or surface impurities, shield his apparatus from all unwanted irradiation, cool his detector to the lowest attainable temperatures to eliminate all thermal fluctuations; yet there is still an irreducible minimum of noise that comes with the radiation he receives as a signal.

Heat and Disorder

Not all fluctuations manifest themselves directly as deviations from a mean number of electrons, photons, or atoms. In other words, the procedure we have adopted so far for the interpretation and determination of noise in terms of an rms-deviation $\langle \Delta n^2 \rangle$ is unsuitable in certain instances. We refer to the important class of thermal fluctuations, since aspects of its laws of randomness are apparently different from those we have been discussing.

At this point we must recall the intimate connection between thermal quantities—heat content and temperature—and the concept of *disorder*. The relationship between heat and disorder is not obvious in phenomena occurring on a macroscopic scale. Temperature, for example, reveals itself merely through the sense of touch, or through the expansion of gases, liquids, or solids. Again, heat content is a form of energy which increases monotonically (but not always linearly) with temperature. All other forms of energy can be and ultimately are completely transformed into heat energy. However, the inverse is *not* true; heat cannot be *completely* converted into other forms of energy; the process of "degenerating" mechanical, electrical, or nuclear

170

energy into thermal forms is *irreversible* in that no process or machine, however ingenious, can restore the original state. Here we have the first hint of a connection with disorder; it is characteristic also that transformations from order to disorder are irreversible. For instance, it is entirely possible for a chess player to upset his game and scramble the chessmen by shaking the table to avoid impending defeat; it would be an unbelievable accomplishment to shake a set of fallen chessmen into a winning position. Many examples in physics show that a system, left to itself, progresses unidirectionally from order to disorder. The diffusion of gases, for example, always proceeds toward intermixing the components, never toward separating them. Similarly, an isolated system of hot and cold bodies spontaneously tends toward equilibrium with all temperatures equal; on the other hand, no instance has ever been recorded of a glass of lukewarm water separating itself into a boiling and a freezing portion. All these considerations, concerned as they are with macroscopic phenomena, imply indirectly the relationship between heat and disorder. But a real understanding of the nature of this interconnection can only be gained from the atomistic picture that has evolved from theory and experiment.

This situation is always best explained for the case of ideal gases. We are dealing here with the microcosmic model of single atoms in random motion, behaving much like billiard balls, since they move in straight lines until they collide and exchange kinetic energy; otherwise they have no attraction or repulsion for each other. The kinetic energy is thus forever changing from one collision to the next, or from one atom to the next, but the mean value at least has a definite magnitude according to the equipartition law: the mean kinetic energy for each possible component of motion (*degree of freedom*) is $\frac{1}{2} kT$; since space is three-dimensional, the total per atom amounts to $\frac{3}{2} kT$. Here T is the absolute temperature, and k is the Boltzmann constant (1.38×10^{-16} erg/deg). Thus, an atomistic interpretation of heat energy in ideal gases is actually rather simple. The mean kinetic energy per atom $mv^2/2$ equals $\frac{3}{2} kT$; the total thermal content is then the sum of all these kinetic energies, $3NkT/2$ for N atoms. For instance, we can compute from the relationships given so far that the mean velocity (rms) of neon atoms at room temperature is about 10^5 cm/sec (one kilometer per second). This is approximately the velocity of a rifle bullet in flight. The weight of such a bullet is about 20 grams, the weight of a mole of neon gas. (A *mole* is the molecular weight of any substance expressed in grams.) In this situation we compare two systems of equal amounts of mass and velocity, and thus we can state that the kinetic energy of the rifle bullet is about equal to the molar heat content of neon at room temperature. Since a mole of any material contains the same number of molecules, this last statement can be generalized for all rare gases.

Nevertheless, there is a big difference between the two types of energy, even though both are kinetic in nature. In the case of the bullet, the kinetic energy results from atomic velocity components which are identical in amount and direction; in the case of the gas, heat energy in its very essence results from atomic velocities in a state of greatest possible disorder and which, in fact, amount to zero when vectorially added (since the center of gravity is assumed to be at rest with respect to the observer). We can easily transform the orderly motion of the bullet into heat energy, disorderly motion. A partial conversion takes place, at any rate, when the projectile hits its mark, and the conversion into heat is complete if it spends itself in a gaseous or a liquid medium. This process, however, cannot be inverted; it is manifestly impossible to transform the irregular motion of gas molecules *completely* into the kinetic energy of a projectile, and we recognize this as a typical characteristic of a disorder mechanism.

Brownian Movement

The incessant random motion of atomistic particles, which from the microcosmic point of view is the very essence of heat, cannot be observed directly because of the great speed and small size of the atoms. Indirect experimental evidence, however, comes from the observation of thermal fluctuations and noise.

Perhaps the most beautiful demonstration is possible with a phenomenon discovered by the English botanist, Robert Brown, in 1827. His discovery, incidentally, represents one of the earliest proofs of the existence of atoms, although this was not its immediate interpretation. The experiment requires a microscope of sufficient power to allow observation of suspensions or emulsions of very small particles.

India ink, with its distribution of very fine carbon powder, is a suitable material for the purpose, and so is ash dust floating in tobacco smoke if it is trapped in a suitable container. With good illumination, we can then see a lively random motion of the particles. In particular, if we follow the course of an individual particle, we find that it describes a trace, as shown in Fig. 17.2. *Brownian movement* is a *random walk* process: the particle zig-zags in small irregular steps, changing direction each time. It is typical of the random walk process that both the direction and the arrival point are as unpredictable as the path of a man lost in a blinding snow storm. Nevertheless, a statistical prediction is possible. If a large number of displacements is measured, the mean square (the average of their squared values) increases in proportion to time; while the direction is completely random (quasi-isotropic), the most probable distance from the origin is proportional to the square root of the travel time. This law, first postulated by Einstein in 1905, can easily be verified experimentally. It is significant that the phenomena of diffusion, such as the diffusion of one gas into another, or of a salt into a solvent, obey a similar law.

This leads to the rather obvious conclusion that the motion of molecules follows the same laws as the Brownian movement; the only difference is size. The path of a molecule is linear until it collides with another molecule. As the particle diameter increases, the surface increases with its square, and the mass with its cube. This means, first, that the particle of greater surface experiences more collisions per unit time which come, however, from random directions and thus largely tend to cancel each other's effects on the displacement; second, as the mass increases, the mean velocity decreases. Therefore, as we progress

Figure 17.2

173

from molecules with a diameter size of angstroms to colloidal particles in the order of microns, dimensions and speeds are just right to observe directly the effect of the equipartition law. As we go on to macroscopic objects, masses are so large and the cancellation of the random impulses by the enormous number of striking molecules is so complete that Brownian movement is no longer detectable. Of course, the equipartition law is valid regardless of size. Thus, the mean kinetic energy of a rigid body due to the velocity component v_x in the x direction is

$$\frac{mv_x^2}{2} = \frac{kT}{2}.$$

The corresponding relations are valid for components in the y and z directions. The mean energy, $kT/2$, also applies to rotation, vibration, and other degrees of freedom, if the corresponding movements are possible for the particle. These small energies are only observable, and therefore only of concern, if the objects exposed to heat motion are themselves quite small. This is precisely the situation we encounter, however, when we try to probe deeply into microcosmic matter, or when we want to achieve the limit of performance with our tools of detection and measurement.

Thermal Fluctuations

Conclusions about heat content and disorder can be generalized as follows: Suppose a medium contains N particles, each free to assume a position which can be described by m coordinates ($m = 3$ for ideal gases). The system is then characterized by mN degrees of freedom; it takes mN numbers to determine completely the instantaneous configuration of the system. As a result of heat, these mN numbers are random—on a macroscopic scale their values are unpredictable from moment to moment. However, there is a law of equipartition, which states that each degree of freedom is endowed with an average energy of $kT/2$. Thus, the heat content is the total of $mN \times kT/2$ random contributions (in addition to certain "latent" energies for melting, vaporizing, and other phase changes). It follows that any observation or measurement, in so far as it partakes of the energy equilibrium of the medium, is affected by fluctuations as the result of the equipartition

174

law. More specifically, if we expose to the medium a measuring device or system with the equivalent of n degrees of freedom, we encounter a thermal noise level of $nkT/2$, and observations are noise limited to that extent. A mirror galvanometer, for example, has essentially one functional movable part: the mirror which is in rigid connection with a magnetic deflection needle and which is held in equilibrium by a torsional wire. Angular velocity and angular position are the dimensions of motion which are important for measurement during observation. Held in some atmosphere, the mirror then exposes two degrees of freedom to the striking molecules. Hence, it is subject to a "jitter" motion of energy kT. The operation of a mirror galvanometer relies on the light mass and high response of the deflection mechanism. It is apparent that the lowest current that can be measured produces a deflection of the same order as that caused erratically by the kT noise.

Furthermore, this last example is capable of testifying to the marvelous tenacity with which first principles of nature are apt to assert themselves. It would seem an easy matter to stop the "Brownian jitter" in the mirror galvanometer, simply by placing the movable parts in an evacuated chamber, so that no kinetic energy could be transferred to them by colliding molecules. The results of such an attempt are disappointing; motion continues as before, excited from without by the radiation field and the support wire, and from within by the electrons. In other words, the equipartition law cannot be circumvented; whatever means is employed to keep an object at a temperature T—for example, a surrounding, evacuated, yet still radiating enclosure—such means will also communicate to each degree of freedom a fluctuation energy $kT/2$ and, in turn, receive it back from the object.

Thus, regardless of the type of thermal interchange, two aspects of thermal energy always manifest themselves. First, if an object is at a temperature T the mean energy value fluctuates between zero and the order of kT. In other words, $kT/2$ represents both mean and noise level for a single degree of freedom.

How does a system of many atoms behave in this respect? Clearly, if there are n degrees of freedom, we can assume that all of them have direct, or indirect, thermal interchange with the surroundings of the object. Therefore, the heat energy of the object, which on the average is $nkT/2$, must also fluctuate. Since the individual contributions at any instant are random, the total energy of fluctuation is $\sqrt{n}\, kT/2$, according to the mean square deviation law we discussed previously. Now, this heat fluctuation is observable through a fluctuation of temperature as $C\Delta T$, where $C = nk/2$ represents the heat capacity of the object (the energy necessary to increase the temperature of the object by $1°K$ without doing external work). Thus we have:

$$C\Delta T_{\mathrm{rms}} \cong \sqrt{n}\,\frac{kT}{2} = \sqrt{\frac{2C}{k}}\,\frac{kT}{2}.$$

Hence,

$$\langle \Delta T^2 \rangle \cong \frac{kT^2}{2C}.$$

This is a rough derivation, of course, correct by order of magnitude. A more rigorous treatment changes this result by a factor of two (which can be explained in our model by a deviation from randomness in the energy addition, since—as in the galvanometer example—pairs of degrees of freedom add to kT). Thus, for the *temperature noise,* in terms of the mean square fluctuation, we have

$$\langle \Delta T^2 \rangle \cong \frac{kT^2}{C}.$$

This result implies that the temperature of an object is never exactly constant, but fluctuates more and more as samples become smaller with correspondingly smaller heat capacities. Thus, for spherical particles of a micron diameter (where $C \cong 10^{12}\, k$) the temperature is uncertain to about one part in 10^6 on the Kelvin scale—very little, indeed, but setting a definite limit to observation. If the diameter of the particle is a submicroscopic 0.1 micron, the fluctuation is one part in 30,000, or 0.01 degrees at room temperature.

In principle, temperature noise could limit the performance of some of the radiation detectors described in Chapter 11, "Beyond the Limits of Vision," those in which the incident power is first converted into heat and evaluated as a temperature change by some mechanism. In practice, however, other disturbances are apt to be much more important. The ultimate reason is that in a sense temperature noise is a second order effect, consisting of the fluctuation in the state of disorder; it is the noise of noise.

176

Johnson Noise

In 1928, the physicist J. B. Johnson observed a curious thermal agitation of electricity in conductors. The phenomenon consists of a fluctuating voltage generated across the terminals, the magnitude of the effect being independent of the material and of the presence or absence of a current impressed externally. The noise can be demonstrated with an oscilloscope using sufficient amplifier gain, as shown schematically in Fig. 17.3. The mean value of this *Johnson noise* voltage, or the resulting noise current, is obviously zero, since otherwise formidable charges would build up at the terminals. The average noise power, proportional to the square of the voltage, is not zero, but has the value

$$P = kT\Delta f,$$

where Δf is the bandwidth which is being observed. We note that this relation has all the aspects of a universal law: its validity is not restricted to any material, resistance, or magnitude of current, and it is remarkable that it does not make any reference to the fundamental electronic constants of charge and mass, even though it describes an important aspect of electricity.

That the origin of these fluctuations lies in thermal energy—in particular, that of the electrons—was recognized at once, since only thermal agitation could explain the generation of random power of the type described. Furthermore, in 1906 Einstein had already extended his theory of Brownian movement to the thermal diffusion of electrons and had predicted the generation of fluctuating charges in conductors.

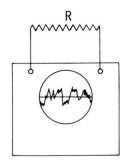

Figure 17.3

There are many ways that lead to the Johnson noise formula; perhaps the most direct and revealing method of describing it follows the general line of reasoning which was first used by Nyquist.

We imagine that the electrons in a conductor of length L between the terminals are capable of performing oscillations—not independently, but cooperatively, like the atoms in the vibrating string shown in Fig. 17.4. Now, this picture applied to solids appears to be in violent contradiction to the one of particles moving in complete disorder and independence. Yet this lack of beauty must be only in the eye of the beholder, for we are able to assert that either model is valid and capable of explaining the observed facts. Therefore, the thermal motion of electrons and atoms in solids must follow from a superposition of their "natural" vibrations, provided all possible modes are taken into consideration. Now, the number of all possible vibrational modes is enormous—even in the one-dimensional case of the vibrating string—a fact that reveals itself at once to the incipient violin player, and alas to his listeners, too. Although very large, the number is finite.

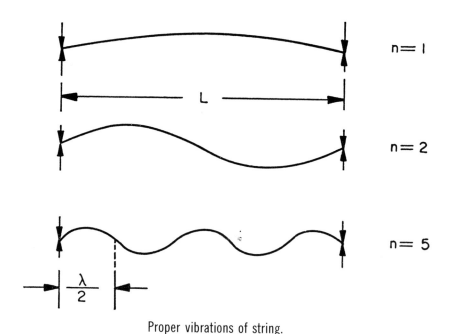

Proper vibrations of string.

Figure 17.4

To explain this concept of modes in a little more detail, we assume that the ends of the string are clamped, as indicated in Fig. 17.4. The vibrations are then the oscillations that all points describe, each with fixed amplitude, although from point to point this amplitude varies sinusoidally. This is the picture of *standing waves*, and it is characteristic that these consist of an integer number n of half-waves between the clamped (or reflecting) ends, so that we can write

$$L = \frac{n\lambda}{2}, \quad \text{or} \quad L = n\frac{v}{2f}.$$

In the second equation we have introduced the frequency f (the pitch) which corresponds to the wavelength λ by virtue of the relation $\lambda f = v$, where v is the velocity of propagation. Of course, in the case of standing waves, propagation has a special meaning: the vibrational mode is constituted of two running waves—the first moves in one direction and then, reflected at the end, returns as the second wave, thus forming the standing wave pattern. Therefore, all possible frequencies are multiples (harmonics) of the fundamental. Nevertheless, there is an upper limit, which is reached when the half-wave is just equal to the inter-atomic distance. The number of possible vibrations is thus equal to the number N of atoms in the string. We may assign two degrees of freedom to each vibration; there are then, all together, $2N$ degrees of freedom available to the motion of the string.

This model, particularly when extended to three dimensions, is very useful in physics for the computation of magnitudes such as that of specific heat, or even of heat radiation.

The string vibrations can be compared with the possible electrical modes in a conductor. It follows from the equation for the allowable number of half-waves, $n = 2f\,L/v$, that there are $4L\Delta f/v$ degrees of freedom in a frequency interval Δf, corresponding to a thermal energy of $2L\,kT\Delta f/v$ for the entire conductor. Of this amount, a fraction $v/2L$ passes each second in each direction through any point of the conductor, including its terminals. Thus, we arrive at the fluctuation power

$$P = \frac{v}{2L} \times \frac{2LkT\Delta f}{v} = kT\Delta f,$$

which, of course, is the Johnson noise formula.

The limitations imposed by these fluctuations are at least as important as those of shot noise. Johnson noise and shot noise cause the "snow" that appears on television tubes when we turn the gain high to receive a distant station.

An important example is the limitation in the measurement of photo-current which, in a range still undisturbed by shot noise, can not compete with the thermal noise generated in the resistors of the ampli-fiers. Thus, there is a need for amplification without the use of resistors, and this principle underlies the cascading of secondary emission stages in photomultipliers. (See Fig. 11.5 of Chapter 11, "Beyond the Limits of Vision.") The electron multiplier makes it possible to measure levels so small that the current is limited only by shot noise. In the limit of response—one photoelectron for each photon—the observation thresh-old is then determined by the photon fluctuations themselves; in other words, by the noise that comes with the signal.

The Meaning of Uncertainty

18

In his famous booklet *What Is Life?* Erwin Schrödinger shows how the rules governing the growth and function of living organisms are, in turn, determined by the principles of physics. He begins with the question, "Why are the atoms so small?" Of course, this is the same as asking, "Why are *we* so big?" The answer is that biological systems must encounter the same type of limitations we have seen at work in all observation and measurement. In other words, the reliability of the physiological apparatus for sensing and transmitting stimuli from the outside world depends again on some signal-to-noise ratio, as determined by random fluctuations. Thus, in the long trial-and-error process of evolution, creatures representing the highest organisms came to be constituted of an enormous number of atoms—so large a number that the correlated fluctuations became sufficiently small under the conditions necessary for survival.

And yet the most important biological structures, the genes in chromosomes, apparently have to conform to somewhat different conditions. From the time of conception, the genes represent the information code, the microcosmic blueprint of the unfolding individual. The most remarkable aspect of the genes is that they come in very small sizes, typically in the order of several hundred angstroms, and have to be regarded in fact as complex organic molecules; nevertheless, they are not only responsible for the inherited characteristics of any particular person, but directly or intermittently for those of all succeeding generations. The shape of a human lip, a defective heart muscle, or even the level of intelligence, all these are anchored in specific configurations of only a few atoms. Yet these submicroscopic entities in the regenerative cells have to survive for many centuries, so that the shape of the particular lip can occur and recur generation after generation, albeit in combination with still other features and other talents that have been acquired by the clan through the ages. That such genetic coding, such divine handwriting, contained as it were in the constellation of atoms, can withstand for so long the battering of thermal agitation bears witness to the stability that even a complex organic molecule can possess. We say that the atoms in such molecules are bonded with a quantized energy of a magnitude which cannot be attained by thermal collisions at body temperatures except at extremely infrequent intervals. Of course, the photons and particles of high-energy radiation, such as from radioactive sources or x rays, are amply capable of altering or destroying the gene arrangement; but again these events are very rare, at least under naturally occurring conditions, for they require a "direct hit" of a tiny cross section by a gamma ray or a proton, or the like. Indeed, such *mutations,* as the abrupt changes of hereditary characteristics are called, happen naturally just often enough so that, besides a great number of surviving misfits, an occasional evolutionary upstart also occurs. Thus we see that the different rules governing the size of biological structures actually reflect different functions; the media of sensing must be flexible, which requires, as we have shown, a large number of atoms; the genetic material must be rigid, which demands small size.

There is still another aspect of the physical limits of physiological sensing and observing. The eyes of all animals, except insects, project an image of the observed scene onto the retina by means of a lens. Now, from the point of view of fluctuation theory, even a relatively small eye might suffice. On a retina area as small as one square millimeter, there is still space for about 10^{13} to 10^{14} atoms arranged in a single layer. But here a more important limit comes into play. The wavelength of visible light is in the order of 6,000 angstroms, a length covering from 2,000 to 6,000 atoms. The retina contains a large number—in the order of several millions—of light-sensitive cells, mainly the cones for daylight vision in color, and the far more sparsely distributed rods for night perception. Each of these cells is capable of transmitting a separate light impression to the brain. For this to be the case, the linear dimension of the cell has to be large compared to the wavelength— typically in the order of several microns. Of course, this sets a lower limit for the size of the eye if it is to be capable of perceiving a given field of view with sufficient detail, or *resolution*. Small birds, therefore, have eyes that are very large compared with their body size; and in insects there is an altogether different principle of seeing. On the other hand, a larger sized eye than that commensurate with functional necessity can have drawbacks—greater exposure to possible injury, for instance.

Similar principles probably also govern the size of genes in chromosomes. The genes can be of extremely small size, determined by the minimum number of atoms held in strongly-bonded configurations. Again, a larger than necessary size of the genetic material reduces its chances of survival; the probability of an encounter with a gamma quantum increases with size, as does the likelihood of other events causing mutations. We have mentioned the role of mutations in evolution; a control of stability may well be active in an "equilibrium" size of the genes. In this, as in any other characteristic, biological systems display their adaptation to the laws of physics and their universal constants.

It is clear that the elementary limitation, discussed in connection with the minimum size of the rods and cones of the retina, must also play a role in various kinds of optical instrumentation. More generally stated, it is not possible to measure an individual quantity smaller than the atomistic dimensions of the medium used for such measurement. This would amount to lifting a needle with a pitchfork, even if it could be found in a haystack.

The optical case is best illustrated by the ultimate limitation of the microscope. (See Fig. 18.1) The length of an object, or the position x of a point, cannot be determined closer than within about a wavelength λ. More precisely, this uncertainty of length or position is obtained from considerations of physical optics as

$$\Delta x \approx \frac{\lambda}{\sin \alpha},$$

where α is the aperture angle, which should be as large as possible; but in any event, $\sin \alpha$ cannot exceed unity. Thus, the only possibility that offers itself for increasing resolution is decreasing the wavelength.

An interesting opportunity is available here. When light travels through a transparent medium, its velocity and wavelength are reduced

183

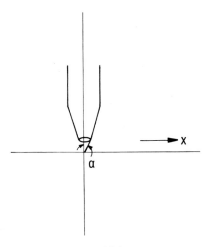

Figure 18.1

by a factor n, the index of refraction. Thus, if a suitable liquid is suspended between the objective lens of the microscope and the viewed object, the uncertainty of position is reduced by the factor n. We then speak of an *immersion microscope* with a *numerical aperture n* sin α. A typical value for the numerical aperture is 1.4, so that objects of about 2,500 angstrom diameter can still be resolved with blue light.

For further improvements of a similar kind, ultraviolet microscopes are used in combination with various devices to convert the ultraviolet image into a visible pattern. In principle, we can continue on to x rays, although such a microscope has to be constructed quite differently. Actually, the x-ray microscope suggests a famous thought-experiment, and the reason is quite pertinent to our discussion.

Suppose we want to determine the position of an electron under such a microscope. We know that we can do this more and more accurately as we decrease the x-ray wavelength. But now an important phenomenon becomes apparent. It is known from theory and experiment that the photons of which electromagnetic radiation consists behave like corpuscles with a momentum $p = mv = h/\lambda$, where Planck's constant $h = 6.62 \times 10^{-27}$ erg $\cdot$ sec. Specifically, the experiment by A. H. Compton proved that x rays scattered by electrons experience an increase in wavelength which could be exactly accounted for by the transfer of such a momentum to the electrons which were

184

loosely bound to atoms in paraffin. Thus we must expect, too, that in our thought-experiment the electron, as viewed by an x-ray quantum, receives a momentum h/λ in random direction. However, only the photons entering the aperture angle α can be observed in the microscope. Therefore, there exists for the electron an uncertainty of momentum in the x-direction which amounts to

$$\Delta p_x \approx \frac{h}{\lambda} \sin \alpha.$$

It follows that we are dealing with two complementary uncertainties—the uncertainty Δx in locating the position x of the electron, and the uncertainty Δp_x in simultaneously determining the momentum p_x. An inspection of the two pertinent equations for Δx and Δp_x reveals that if the measurement of position is made increasingly accurate by the application of smaller wavelengths (and larger $\sin \alpha$), the velocity (or momentum) becomes correspondingly more uncertain, and vice versa. In fact, for the product of the two equations we obtain

$$\Delta x \times \Delta p_x \approx h,$$

the relation known as *Heisenberg's uncertainty principle*.

The validity of this statement is far more general than the specific example would indicate. The position of any atomistic particle can be determined—or can exist, in fact—with a definition or sharpness inversely proportional to that of the velocity. There is also a corresponding relationship between energy and time:

$$\Delta E \Delta t \approx h.$$

In this form, the principle means that to determine the energy of a particle within an error interval of ΔE, it is necessary to take into the bargain an uncertainty of Δt in time, so that an observation period of $\tau = h/\Delta E$ is needed. But the principle goes much deeper, in fact. It asserts that these limitations of accuracy are not merely the result of imperfect measurement and that, moreover, they exist independent of any measurement. In other words, the uncertainty in measurement simply records an uncertainty of nature. For example, a radioactive nucleus may have an energy state E before it decays into a stable isotope. The Heisenberg relation then interprets ΔE as a "fuzziness" of the energy level, and Δt as the mean time during which such a state can be observed, that is, its lifetime. The randomness of radioactive decay, which we have discussed earlier, appears thus as a consequence of the uncertainty principle and is correlated with the sharpness of the corresponding energy states.

The deepest implication of all this is the question of causality, which we mentioned in Chapter 1, "The Purpose of Science." For is not all physical measurement based on the implicit expectation that, if precisely controlled and identically repeated, every sequence of events should also run the selfsame course? And yet here we are being told that on the scale of atomistic events nature itself does not know, and that it is *in principle* impossible to tie together precise conjugate values of individual systems. Therein, then, lies the ultimate limitation of all observation; we have progressed, in fact, to questions for which precise answers do not exist.

Anchor Points of Science

Constants of Physics

19

WE HAVE SEEN that units serve the purpose of standardizing measurement by allowing a comparison to be made between an observed physical variable and a basic reference value. In physics we are concerned with the functional interrelation of different physical variables, such as position and time, volume and temperature, or electric charge, velocity and magnetic field. If these relationships are reproducible, and particularly if their causes and their effects are understood, they are expressed in analytical form as equations (or sometimes inequalities); we then consider them physical laws. The functions will contain the pertinent physical variables, and in addition there will be coefficients or constants—to bridge the different dimensions, if for no other reason. In passing, we note a single exception: units which are directly defined by the equation representing the physical laws. An example is Coulomb's law concerning the force F with which two charges, e_1 and e_2, separated by a distance r, act on each other in a vacuum:

$$F = \frac{e_1 e_2}{r^2}.$$

Unit charge is defined as that which repels an equal charge at 1 cm distance with a force of 1 dyne. The need for a constant is thus eliminated in this instance.

In most cases, however, we need a parameter of conversion. The law of Gay-Lussac is a particularly simple example. It is written

$$v = v_0(1 + \alpha t),$$

and states that a volume v_0 of an ideal gas at a temperature $t = 0°C$ expands to a volume v at a higher temperature t at the fractional rate of α per degree centigrade. Thus, aside from the variables v and t, a constant has been introduced, or rather a *coefficient*, as one usually calls such parameters which are characteristic of a substance or system.

It is interesting to follow this example further, by choosing a different zero for the temperature scale. When we set

$$T = t + \frac{1}{\alpha},$$

Gay-Lussac's law assumes the simple form

$$v = \alpha v_o T.$$

This equation also reveals the new temperature scale as *absolute*, because at $T = 0$, the volume has also become zero, so that this point represents the lowest temperature a gas can assume.

It is possible to widen the scope of this law at once to include two additional functional relationships. The first concerns pressure and volume and takes the form $pv = \text{const}$ (the law of Boyle-Mariotte). The second is Avogadro's statement that different ideal gases of the same volume contain the same number of molecules under otherwise equal conditions of temperature and pressure. In particular, if we refer to a *mole* (the molecular weight in grams), we deal with the same number of molecules (Avogadro's number $N_o = 6.025 \times 10^{23}/\text{mole}$) and, therefore, also with the same volume (at $T = 273°K$, $P = 1$ atm., and $V = 22.4 \times 10^3$ cc). Thus, we arrive at a combined equation of state for all ideal gases:

$$PV = RT.$$

We have used the capital letters P and V to indicate molar pressure and volume, respectively. In this equation, R ($= 8.31 \times 10^7$ erg/mole deg) is of special interest. This is called the *universal gas constant*, because its magnitude is a pivot point in all calculations that concern gases. However, R can be still further reduced. Using Avogadro's number N_o, we may write

$$R = N_o k,$$

where k is the Boltzmann constant, discussed in Chapter 17, "More and More Noise." We mentioned k in connection with the equipartition law; it represents twice the specific heat per degree of freedom. In a sense, we have arrived at a more *fundamental constant* than R, since k refers to a single atom rather than to the mass of the molecular weight in grams, or to any other constant.

The Boltzmann constant appears not only in the theory of gases, but is also directly or implicitly contained in all relationships where a thermal process plays a role. In fact, sometimes we are reminded only by the presence of the factor k that temperature is involved in any way. We find this fundamental constant in apparently diverse connections, such as the Boltzmann factor, $\exp(-E/kT)$, which appears in the barometric height formula and in all situations where particles overcome an energy hurdle under the compulsion of thermal energy; the expressions for heat transfer by radiation or conduction; the constants for mobility and diffusion; and the formulas occurring in all particle statistics.

It is apparent from examples like the gas law that certain basic constants are common to many laws and bridge, in fact, many fields. We can show this process with a flow chart:

Units → Coefficients (practical constants) →
$$\text{Universal Constants} \rightarrow \text{Fundamental Constants}$$

This does not mean that the fundamental constants arise solely as the common denominator of various relationships; they do have, in fact, a distinct physical and individual meaning. The speed of light in its own right, for instance, has been the object of ingenious measurements for centuries—long before it was realized that it recurred in an enormous number of connections. Nevertheless, it cannot be overemphasized that the fundamental constants represent pivot points of quantitative physics, points on which its entire structure is secured. It follows that the number of such key points must be much smaller than the number of ordinary constants. Actually, the whole of physics rests on only about a dozen data—or at least so we can state in principle.

A list of fundamental constants, and the universal constants derived from them, is compiled in Table 19.1. We must admit an important uncertainty, however. In the widening frontier of nuclear physics, it is by no means clear which basic quantities—pertaining to many new particles—are quantitatively derivable from the same origin. At present, any enumeration must necessarily be arbitrary. In Table 19.1 we cite

TABLE 19.I

Values from the Least Square Adjustment of Cohen, DuMond, and McNish†

Fundamental Constants

c	velocity of light	2.997925×10^{10} cm sec^{-1}
e	electronic charge	4.80296×10^{-10} esu
G	Gravitation constant	6.670×10^{-8} dyne cm^2 gm^{-2}
h	Planck constant	6.62554×10^{-27} erg sec
k	Boltzmann constant	1.38053×10^{-16} erg deg^{-1}
m	electron rest mass	9.10904×10^{-28} gm
M_p	mass of proton	1.671867×10^{-24} gm
N_o	Avogadro's number	6.02257×10^{23} mole^{-1}

Universal Constants

$R = N_o k$	gas constant per mole	8.31432×10^7 erg deg^{-1} mole^{-1}
$F = 10N_o e/c$	Faraday's constant	9.64873×10^4 coul gm-equiv^{-1}
e/m	specific electronic charge	5.272741×10^{17} esu gm^{-1}
$r_o = e^2/mc^2$	classical radius of electron	2.81776×10^{-13} cm
$a_0 = h^2/4\pi^2 me^2$	first Bohr radius	5.291659×10^{-9} cm
$\alpha = 2\pi e^2/hc$	fine structure constant	$1/137.043 = 7.29720 \times 10^{-3}$
$\sigma = 2\pi^5 k^4/15c^2 h^3$	Stefan-Boltzmann constant	5.6697×10^{-5} erg cm^{-2} deg^{-4} sec^{-1}
$\lambda_{ce} = h/mc$	Compton wavelength of electron	2.426206×10^{-10} cm
$\lambda_0 = 300(hc/e)$	wavelength associated with 1 eV° ...	1.239805×10^{-4} cm eV
$v_o = [(2/300)(e/m)]^{1/2}$	speed of 1 eV electron	5.93188×10^7 cm sec^{-1}
mc^2	energy equivalent of electron mass	5.110058×10^5 eV m^{-1}
$e/300$	energy associated with 1 eV	1.602095×10^{-12} ergs (eV)$^{-1}$

° 1 volt equals 1/300 electrostatic units of potential.

† See also R. D. Huntoon, *Handbook of Chemistry and Physics*, 44th ed., Chemical Rubber Publishing Co., Cleveland, Ohio, 1962–1963.

only a small number of particles; surely, a key to unifying the particle system will be found in the future.

The gravitation constant G is a fundamental constant a little apart from the others. It appears only in one basic relationship—Newton's law of attraction F between bodies of mass M_1 and M_2 at a distance r^2 from each other:

$$F = G\frac{M_1 M_2}{r^2} \, .$$

G is defined by this equation as a coefficient which at the same time is a fundamental constant. The acceleration g is derived from G, and either g or a balance measuring the horizontal force between two large, delicately suspended masses can be used to determine the gravitational constant.

Aside from the requirements of experimental physics, the requirements of theory also depend on the fundamental constants as pivot points of the entire scientific structure. Thus, it is of special importance to view critically their most essential attribute, and to ask: *are they really constant?* Of course, this question has been answered—but answered for only a limited time and space: a few centuries and the extent of our planetary system.

In "The Methods of Science," Chapter 3, we described Michelson's experiment—the measurement of the speed of light in various directions —and the consequences for twentieth-century physics, an example for the importance of a constant. In general it is possible to measure a fundamental constant by two or more methods. If then a systematic difference is found, one not attributable to random errors, an unexpected feature is revealed by nature. It may be minor; a second-order perturbation may be responsible for the deviation. On the other hand, while small in size, the difference may be explainable only by some new and bold assumption. The mass defect of atomic weights is an example. Instead of simply being multiples of the proton mass, atoms of all the various isotopes are lighter—by a small fraction—than such multiples. The difference, then, had to be ascribed to the nuclear binding energy, which appeared as the equivalent of the mass defect, $E = mc^2$. To a certain extent, these and other findings were accidental; if a systematic search is undertaken, we can expect even greater surprises.

Atomic Constants

THE DAWN of atomic physics toward the close of the nineteenth century brought about a new era in scientific measurement. Since then, tremendous strides have been made in measurement of the physical world. First, scientists began to explore the atom, then the nucleus, and today they are engaged in an all-out attack—studying the particles that compose the atomic nucleus, and measuring the forces between subatomic particles.

By the turn of the century, the atomic theory of matter was well established, largely based on evidence from chemical reactions and from the kinetic theory of gases. The electrical nature of matter was also apparent from the studies of electrical discharges, which were receiving widespread investigation, including the experiments of such eminent scientists as Heinrich Hertz, Wilhelm Roentgen, J. W. Hittorf, Sir William Crooks, and many others. The work of these men set the stage for the celebrated experiment of J. J. Thompson in his discovery of the electron.

A significant milestone in scientific investigation, the discovery of the electron, was accomplished with a very simple arrangement, judged by today's standard, which makes it a truly noteworthy achievement. The apparatus used is shown in Fig. 20.1.

Electrically charged particles emitted by a cathode C were collimated into a thin "pencil" by the defining slits A and B. This ray of particles was then passed between two parallel plates D and E of length l, to which a voltage could be applied. At the end of the tube, a phosphorescent screen indicated the position of the beam. When a voltage was applied to the plates, the beam underwent a deflection θ. If now the velocity of the particles is v, the time required for a particle to pass between the plates is l/v. Assuming the electric intensity between the

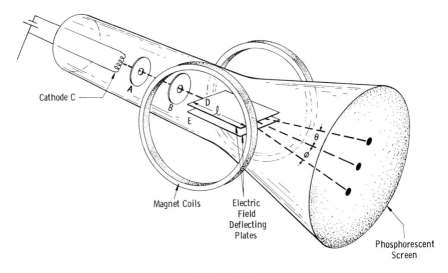

Figure 20.1

plates is E, the velocity in the direction of E is given by $\dfrac{Ee}{m}\dfrac{l}{v}$, and the angle θ is then expressed as $\theta = \dfrac{Ee}{m}\dfrac{l}{v^2}$.

A magnetic field H, imposed on this region by two external coils in such a way that the magnetic field is at right angles to the electric field, deflects the particles in the opposite direction. The velocity in this direction, given by $\dfrac{eHv}{m}\dfrac{l}{v}$, is opposite in direction to that given by the electric field. Since the same forward velocity prevails in the absence of the electric field, the particles are deflected through an angle Φ given by

$$\Phi = \frac{He}{m}\frac{l}{v}.$$

From the equations

$$v = \frac{\Phi}{\theta}\frac{E}{H} \quad \text{and} \quad \frac{m}{e} = \frac{H^2\theta}{E\Phi^2}\,l,$$

Thompson found that m/e was independent of any gas introduced into the tube, and also independent of the nature of the cathode. On the basis of this and other evidence, he concluded that the particles were

196

electrons, and he obtained a value of 1.3×10^{-7} gram per emu (electromagnetic unit). According to the best value accepted today, this is in error only by a factor of two.

Once Thompson had identified the electron, it was only natural that someone should try to determine its properties. Since Thompson's experiment already gave the mass-to-charge ratio, the next obvious step was to determine the mass and the electric charge separately. The easiest way to study mass is from its equivalence to weight, but the mass of the electron is so small that it is impossible to measure an acceleration due to a gravitational field. However, the accelerations caused by forces of electric and magnetic fields acting on charges *are* measurable. Hence, of necessity the approach must involve the electric charge. It follows that determining the electric charge is the most obvious experiment. Working in his laboratory with J. S. E. Townsend, Thompson obtained for the electric charge a value of about 3×10^{-10} esu (electrostatic units). He based this value on observations of the movements of clouds of ionized water vapor between the plates of a condenser, where the settling rate under gravity could be compared to the acceleration under the influence of an electric field.

It remained for R. A. Millikan, however, to devise a method for accurately measuring this charge of the electrons. His precise experiment is one of the great classics of physics. Millikan's idea was essentially the same as Thompson's; a diagram of his apparatus is shown in Fig. 20.2. With the atomizer A, clouds of fine oil droplets were blown into the dust-free chamber C, containing brass air condenser plates M and N, meticulously ground so that their separation never varied by more than 0.02 mm. Oil droplets, allowed to fall into the space between the plates, were illuminated as a narrow beam of light entered the condenser through one port, passed between the plates, and emerged from a second port. A short-focus telescope occupied the third port. Millikan wrote that the oil drop's appearance was ". . . that of a brilliant star on a black background."

Of course, under the action of gravity, the drop fell toward the lower plate, and because the drop was so small, the air resistance made the velocity of its fall constant. Before the droplet had a chance to reach the lower plate, however, the battery B produced an electric field (3,000 to 8,000 volts per centimeter) in the space between the condenser

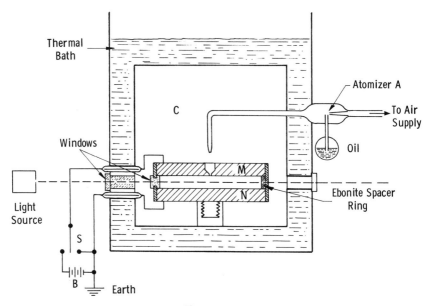

Figure 20.2

plates. The oil drop, electrically charged, was pulled upward, but before it could reach the top plate, a shorting switch S removed the electric field. In this way the same drop could be reversed several times in its ascent and descent, until it lost its charge by catching an ion of positive charge which normally exists in air, or can be formed by the light source.

It is possible, of course, for a droplet to have more than one unit of charge, and hence its velocity v_1 under the influence of the electric field E will be proportional to the total charge Ne. The relationship between the apparent mass M, the charge Ne which it carries, its velocity v_1 due to gravity alone, and its velocity v_2 under the additional influence of the electric field E is given by

$$\frac{v_1}{v_2} = \frac{Mg}{ENe - Mg} \quad \text{or} \quad e = \frac{1}{N}\left[\frac{Mg}{E}\left(\frac{v_1 + v_2}{v_1}\right)\right].$$

The only assumption here is that the velocity of the drop is proportional to the forces acting on it.

If the drop holds multiple charges, and if it captures an ion during its ascent, its velocity suddenly changes from v_2 to v_2', so that

198

$$N_2e - N_1e = \frac{Mg}{E}\left(\frac{v_2' - v_2}{v_1}\right).$$

Since Mg/Ev_1 is a constant for each individual drop (as long as no evaporation takes place), any change in the charges is always proportional to $v_2' - v_2$, that is, the change in the droplet's upward velocity under the influence of the field E.

In this way Millikan showed that the changes in velocity, and hence the change in total charges, were always multiples (usually no greater than two or three) of a constant base value, to within the uncertainty of his transit time measurements. To quote his own words, he demonstrated that ". . . here, then, is direct, unimpeachable proof that the electron is not a 'statistical mean,' but rather the electrical charges found on ions all have exactly the same value or else small exact multiples of that value."

In order to obtain the absolute value of the charge, it was necessary to determine a provisional estimate of the value of M in the last equation. This required using Stokes' formula for the behavior of a spherical object falling through a viscous medium. In its simplest form, this states that if μ is the coefficient of viscosity of the medium, F is the force acting on a spherical drop of radius a, and v is the velocity with which the drop moves under the action of that force, then

$$F = 6\pi\mu av.$$

Now, if σ is the density of the drop, and if ρ is the density of the medium, then

$$M = \frac{4\pi}{3} a^3(\sigma - \rho),$$

which takes into account the buoyancy effect.

From a consideration of the forces acting on the droplet, it is possible to compute its radius and hence its mass. Therefore, the value of the electron charge can be determined from a measurement of the velocities v_1 and v_2 and the electric field strength E, if the values for the density of the oil σ, the density of the air ρ, and the viscosity of the air μ are known.

Millikan's final value $(4.770 \pm 0.005 \times 10^{-10}$ abs. esu) was the mean result of observations over a two-year period on twenty-five droplets, varying in radius from 23.4×10^{-5} cm to 12.2×10^{-5} cm, and at air pressures from normal atmospheric to 20.5 cm of mercury.

Although it appeared that this experiment was an example of the most attentive care to minute detail, it was shown later that one factor, the viscosity of the air, was in error. In spite of this, however, Millikan's result compares favorably with today's accepted value of $(4.80296 \pm .00006) \times 10^{-10}$ esu. This is the least squares' adjusted value obtained from several observers using a variety of techniques and it attests to the excellence of an experiment performed over fifty years ago. Millikan was within 0.7 per cent of the least squares' adjusted value.

Using $(5.27305 \pm 0.00007) \times 10^{17}$ esu per gram for the e/m ratio, and $(4.80296 \pm 0.00006) \times 10^{-10}$ esu for the value of the electronic charge, we obtain $(9.10904 \pm 0.00013) \times 10^{-28}$ grams for the *rest mass* of the electron. The rest mass is specified, because the theory of relativity, as discussed in "The Methods of Science," Chapter 3, states that the mass of a body is determined by its velocity, and is given by

$$m = \frac{m_o}{\sqrt{1 - v^2/c^2}},$$

where m_o is the rest mass, v is the velocity of the particle, and c is the velocity of light. For most cases, v^2/c^2 is such a small number that the mass m is almost identical to the rest mass m_o.

In the new high-energy machines used in nuclear physics, however, particles are accelerated to velocities approaching the speed of light, and their mass changes significantly. Corrective measures must be taken to compensate for this change in mass.

With mass spectrometers, which we discussed earlier, it is possible to determine precisely the charge-to-mass ratio for various ions, as well as the mass of the proton, using the value of the electronic charge. The proton is then compared with its isotope, the *deuteron*, from which the mass of deuterium is obtained. This, in turn, is compared with the helium ion to determine the mass of helium. By comparing $(He^4)^+$ with the triply-charged carbon ion, we arrive at the mass of carbon (mass 12). In this manner, the mass of all light elements has been calculated.

Sir James Chadwick ascertained in 1932 that the radiation given off when beryllium was bombarded with alpha-particles (helium ions) was not gamma rays, as had been supposed, but a neutral particle, subsequently called the *neutron*. Knowing accurately the masses of the light elements, by measuring the kinetic energy (KE) of the reaction particles he was able to calculate the mass of the neutron, $_0n^1$, from reactions such as the following relations:

$$Be^9 + He^4 + KE = C^{12} + {_0}n^1 + KE$$
$$B^{11} + He^4 + KE = N^{14} + {_0}n^1 + KE$$

Since the masses of Be^9, He^4, C^{12}, B^{11}, and N^{14} were known, Chadwick was able to state: "Allowing for errors in the mass measurements, it appears that the mass of the neutron cannot be less than 1.003 and that it probably lies between 1.005 and 1.008." These masses, of course, were atomic mass units (amu) in which the proton mass M_p is $1.00727663 \pm .00000008$ amu. Today the best accepted value of the neutron's mass is 1.008982 ± 0.000003 amu or $(1.67474 \pm 0.00010) \times 10^{-24}$ grams.

Although in 1920 Ernest Rutherford proposed a neutron composed of a proton and an electron in close combination, and Chadwick concluded that his own experiments were in reasonable agreement with this view, scientists today do not agree about the nature of this particle. Some still hold to Rutherford's view, while others believe that the neutron is a fundamental particle. It remains for future experiments to settle the controversy.

Planck's Constant

21

JUST AS THE atomistic nature of matter is basically represented by the proton mass M_p, and the atomistic nature of electricity by the electronic charge e, so the discreteness of energy has its elementary building block in the Planck constant h. For it will be shown in the following that all energy, radiating or oscillating at frequency ν, exists only in "parcels" of $h\nu$. The circumstances surrounding the discovery of the quantization of energy and the concept of that constant are more intricate, however, than the ideas about the atomism of mass and charge. By way of introduction, we will sketch briefly the context within which the constant, along with quantum theory, came into existence.

One of the most vexing problems that confronted theoretical physicists at the end of the nineteenth century was to interpret the various features of incandescent radiation, the laws by which the intensity of emitted light varies continuously through the spectrum, with a maximum at a wavelength that shifts to the blue at higher temperatures. Now, the model used for the explanation was this: The glowing body consists of *radiating dipoles* (and we may imagine these as oscillating atoms and electrons) which are capable of vibrating in a very large number of modes—similar to those of the vibrating string we described earlier. In this way, we can explain a spectral continuum with no upper limit for the frequency of radiation. The argument of classical physics was that each oscillator could vary continuously in amplitude; the average dipole energy, according to the equipartition law, would then be kT. This was the state of theory at the end of the nineteenth century; but it was also realized that the consequences of this theory collided violently with observation. For if this argument is carried to its logical conclusion, the mean energy of any mode, regardless of how high its frequency, would have the value kT and the incandescent spectrum, instead of exhibiting a maximum, would increase beyond the ultraviolet without limits (causing the so-called *ultraviolet catastrophe*).

All these difficulties and others were solved at one stroke when Max Planck postulated in 1900 that the oscillators could assume energy only in quantized or discrete amounts. This energy quantum for an oscillator vibrating at frequency v equals hv, where h appears as a constant of proportionality with the dimension of *action* (erg seconds). The reason the radiation law is radically changed by such a postulate is that it modifies the equipartition law to quite an extent. Any degree of freedom in the oscillator ensemble can now accept energy only in parceled amounts. For this reason, the more energetic modes will not be excited at all. The result is that instead of a mean energy $\bar{\epsilon}$ equal to kT for each oscillator, the quantum theory yields the value

$$\bar{\epsilon} = \frac{hv}{e^{hv/kT}-1}.$$

For small quanta hv, this value approaches the classical kT; but if hv is not negligible compared with kT, $\bar{\epsilon}$ is always smaller than the classical value. This can be seen from a power expansion of the exponential in the denominator:

$$\bar{\epsilon} = \frac{hv}{\left[1 + \dfrac{hv}{kT} + \dfrac{1}{2!}\left(\dfrac{hv}{kT}\right)^2 + \dfrac{1}{3!}\left(\dfrac{hv}{kT}\right)^3 + \right] - 1}$$

$$= \frac{kT}{1 + \dfrac{hv}{2kT} + \dfrac{1}{6}\left(\dfrac{hv}{kT}\right)^2 + \cdots}.$$

For large values of hv, $\bar{\epsilon}$ tends toward zero, and the oscillator is likely not to be excited at all by thermal agitation, so that the heat radiation will vanish at the blue end of the spectrum.

If Max Planck initiated a scientific revolution, Einstein completed it. Einstein concluded that dipoles not only must exist in quantized amounts of energy, they also must absorb and emit radiation in parcels of hv. In other words, light consists of quantized particles called *photons*. This conclusion, in turn, led at once to an understanding of the photoelectric effect. Photons incident on a surface can communicate their energy ($h\nu$) to an electron, and if the energy is large enough, it suffices to tear the electron out of the solid bond. We call this energy of bonding the *work function* φ. Any excess of photon energy appears as kinetic energy. This process is described by Einstein's equation for the photo-electric effect:

$$h\nu = \varphi + \frac{m}{2} v^2 = \varphi + eV.$$

Here we have set $mv^2/2$ equal to the potential energy eV, where V is the voltage capable of accelerating an electron from rest to a velocity v or retarding it from v to zero. The Einstein equation can be read in different ways, and each of these has been the major sustenance of entire industries. For example, the limiting case of $v = 0$ yields the threshold frequency for obtaining photoelectrons, a basic relation for the design of photoemitting and photoconducting cells. However, if we write that equation in the form

$$eV = h\nu - \varphi,$$

we obtain the condition for the inverse process, the production of x rays of frequency ν by the bombardment of a surface with electrons of voltage V from a cathode with the work function φ. We mention in passing that this aspect of Einstein's equation, because of the large ν's, prescribes the need for high-voltage transformers in the x-ray industry.

All of this is pertinent to our present discussion, since each of these processes has been used to determine the fundamental constant h. The various methods are not equally accurate, and all of them can determine h only in combination with other fundamental constants.

The most accurate results are obtained by means of the effect mentioned last—the production of x rays from the electron bombardment of a metal surface. This is called the *Short Wavelength Limit* determination because not all of the electron energy eV is converted into photon generation; some losses occur in the form of residual electron velocity, and from other causes which result in heating the metal. This brings about, therefore, an x-ray spectrum of all possible wavelengths (a *bremsstrahlung continuum*) up to a limit of highest frequency ν_m, or shortest wavelength, and it is this edge for which the relationship

$$h\nu_m = eV + \varphi_{\text{cath}}$$

has to be used. Typical values for the applied voltage V are in the order of 50 kilovolts. By comparison, the work function φ of a few volts is quite small. The supply of the energy φ is furnished by the heat which "lifts" the electrons in the cathode to such an energy that some can escape. This amount then is added to the voltage applied across the x-ray tube.

In actual measurement, an important mode of operation is to observe a fixed wavelength and then sweep the voltage through the critical region. Having thus determined the limit voltage V, a value for h/e is obtained. Of course, if we consider e as given, h is at once available. In fact, however, the electronic charge is directly measured with less accuracy than h/e. This is an example for a general situation, because many atomic constants can be measured more accurately as implicit expressions, in other words, in combination with each other, such as e/m, h/m, h/k, or me^4/h^3. It is possible, of course, to use three determinations, for instance, h/e, e/m, and h/m, to arrive at three individual constants—e, h, and m. However, a more refined system makes simultaneous use of a large number of such input combinations. This is done in *isometric consistency charts*, in which slight deviations from mutual compatibility between the many functions are minimized by the Least Square Method.

206

How Constant Are the Constants?

THE SYSTEM of units, to which we have tied the fundamental constants through physical laws, are in themselves derived from dimensions of the planet Earth. As explained in Chapter 4, "A Standard Language," the *centimeter* follows indirectly from the circumference of the globe, the *second* from its period of revolution, and the *gram* from the mass of a cubic centimeter of water. Of course, all this has been tidied up a bit so that there can be no ambiguity about the actual standards used. Nevertheless, this system of units, although chosen by international agreement, is arbitrary because it is not defined by immutable physical laws and constants. It may also be argued that the precision with which the units are standardized fails to match the accuracy with which it is possible, or will be possible, to measure them.

For these reasons it would seem more consistent with the needs and methods of physics to redefine the units in terms of the basic constants. To a certain extent, this has been accomplished by international convention. The wavelengths of certain spectral lines are, by orders of magnitude, more sharply determined than the length of the standard platinum-iridium bar. Thus, in 1927 it was agreed to set a meter equal to 1,553,164.13 wavelengths of the red cadmium line. Of course, since then even more sharply defined wavelengths have become available, and it seems questionable if at any time we can be satisfied with standards derived in this manner.

There are, however, the fundamental constants. Would it not be possible to anchor not just the quantitative system of physics but also the elementary units to these values, which presumably are unchangeable in all time and space? This has indeed been proposed by a number of theoretical physicists. Planck, for instance, suggested as such *natural units* combinations of the gravitation constant G, the speed of light, c, the Boltzmann k, and h, in the following way:

$$[t] = \sqrt{\frac{Gh}{c^5}} = 1.35 \times 10^{-43} \text{ sec} \quad [m] = \sqrt{\frac{ch}{G}} = 5.45 \times 10^{-5} \text{ gm}$$

$$[l] = \sqrt{\frac{Gh}{c^3}} = 4.05 \times 10^{-33} \text{ cm} \quad [T] = \sqrt{\frac{c^5h}{G}} = 3.56 \times 10^{32} \text{ degree}$$

for time, length, mass, and temperature, respectively. How sharply are the natural units defined? The objections against the geodesically derived units are eliminated here; there is nothing arbitrary in the choice of fundamental constants, and the accuracy of measurement is always commensurate with the precision to which the constants can be determined.

And yet, at the very moment when such a solution could accommodate the ever-increasing accuracy with which the dimensions of time and length can be measured, doubts begin to arise about the invariance of the fundamental constants. Let's see how such a situation could develop.

To be sure, the source of this skeptical attitude is not new. For almost a century physics had a skeleton in its closet in the form of Ernst Mach's principle, which proposes that the concepts of motion have no meaning unless such motion is referred to a system of surrounding bodies and, more particularly, that the inertial force experienced by an accelerated body can be interpreted as gravitation exerted by the surrounding universe. Now, such thoughts have a disturbing quality for the physicist, who puts his faith in the proposition that the dynamics phenomena he observes in the peace of his laboratory are principally undisturbed by events millions of light-years away in an expanding universe. That such an effect may exist for the gravitation constant G has been considered by R. H. Dicke, among others, who suggested, as a possible consequence of Mach's principle, the relation

$$\frac{GM}{rc^2} \sim 1,$$

in which c is the speed of light and M and r total mass and radius, respectively, of the "visible" universe (that is, the part of the cosmos revealed to us so far by signals arriving with the speed of light). If we assume, for instance, that by virtue of an expanding universe the "acting" mass of the universe increases with time at a higher power than does the radius, then it would follow that the gravitation constant decreases with time.

Such an effect, if found to exist, would not be limited to gravitation. As far as the natural units are concerned, they are linked to G as an input value. Of course, the units suggested by Planck contained G, if for no other reason than because no fundamental mass constants had been established at the time. However, even after such atomic masses as that of the electron and the proton have been identified, their application to natural units is certainly not preferable, and at best equivalent, to that of G.

Therefore, if the gravitation constant is not invariant in time and space, the natural units, too, will not be constant; and although such effects may be too small to detect, the principal justification of the natural units may now be in question.

We have to add to this an important suspicion: G is not only physically interrelated to the fundamental atomic constants, but such functional connection is in itself time-and-space variant. P. A. M. Dirac drew inferences of this kind from the so-called *Eddington numbers,* which are dimensionless ratios of such magnitudes as the Coulomb force and the gravitational attraction between electron and proton; or the age of the universe and a unit of atomic time, e^2/mc^3; and the square root of the mass of the universe and that of the proton mass. These ratios contain the fundamental constants, together with the age T and the radius $r = Tc$ of the universe, and they all amount to the same order of magnitude, about 10^{39}-10^{40}. If these numbers truly represent constants, then as T and r vary, the fundamental constants must change accordingly.

Such ideas are still speculative; but ultimately they may be of the utmost importance for the science of atomistic events, as well as that of the cosmos and the interrelation between the two. For important questions—indeed, some of the very questions with which natural philosophy began its labors—still remain unanswered: What is gravitation? How is it connected to atomic forces, and what is the link between these two types of attraction and those of the nucleus? What dimensions and constants will finally prove to be invariant in time and space, providing physics with reference systems of absolute rest?

Appendix:
A Brief Review of Calculus

From time to time we have used some of the ideas and notations of differential and integral calculus. For those who may be unfamiliar with the subject, we append this brief review.

The next two paragraphs describe the most common notation of calculus; some may find this sufficient without reading the rest of the discussion.

The principal concept of differential calculus is embodied in the expression dy/dx, which means the instantaneous rate of change of y with respect to x, where y and x are variables so related that the value of y depends on that of x. For example, if y is the distance covered by an object in total time x, dy/dx is the instantaneous rate of change of distance with respect to time; this is usually called velocity. If y is the number of miles that have been covered by a car on x gallons of gasoline, then at any given point dy/dx is the instantaneous rate of change of distance with respect to gasoline consumption, or the instantaneous mileage in miles per gallon. The expression dy/dx is called the *derivative* of y with respect to x, and the process of finding the derivative in a particular case is called differentiation. (In addition to dy/dx, various notations are used for the derivative, such as Dy, $\dot{y}$, or y' when there is no doubt as to what variable plays the role of x; or $f'(x)$ when $f(x)$ stands for the function of x which is also referred to as y; or $\partial y/\partial x$ or $f_x(x, u, v, w)$ when variables other than x are involved but are being held constant.)

In integral calculus, the principal idea is expressed by

$$\int_a^b f(x)dx$$

read, "The definite integral of $f(x)$ with respect to x, from a to b." Here the dx may be regarded as indicating the variable with respect to which

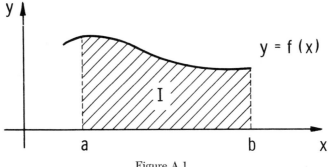

Figure A.1

integration is being carried out. A simple geometric interpretation is provided by Fig. A.1. Here, starting with the function $f(x)$, the "integrand," we draw the graph of $y = f(x)$, and $I = \int_a^b f(x)dx$ is represented by the area between the curve, the x axis, and the vertical lines at $x = a$ and $x = b$. Similarly, if $f(x, y)$ is a function of two variables, $\int_R \int f(x,y)dxdy$ is a frequently used quantity which may be represented by the volume under a surface $z = f(x, y)$ and over a region R in the xy plane.

For those who would prefer a little more explanation, we continue by explaining differential calculus as a study of motion or change. This seems to be the simplest point of view for intuitive presentation, although rigorous treatments are now usually made in other terms.

We say that a variable y is a *function* of a second variable x if the value of y is determined by the value of x. This relationship is often written

$$y = f(x),$$

the expression $f(x)$ being a convenient way to name a function, since we can write, for example, $f(2)$ for the value of $f(x)$ when x is 2, $f(a)$ for the value of $f(x)$ when $x = a$, and so on. Although the letter f is often used here by virtue of being the initial letter of the word "function," other letters are also used. A given problem may involve several functions of x called, for example, $f(x)$, $g(x)$, $F(x)$, $\varphi(x)$.

The simplest functions are the linear functions, and an example is

$$y = \frac{1}{2}x.$$

This expression obviously defines a relation between y and x in which y always has a value that is just half that of x. If coordinate axes are used as in Fig. A.2, the collection of points whose y coordinate is half the x coordinate is referred to as the graph of the function. The graph in this case is a straight line, hence the name "linear" applied to the function. In general, a linear function of x may be recognized by its form $a + bx$, where a and b are constants.

In differential calculus we study functions from the point of view of determining the rate of change of y with respect to x. Consider, for example, the function

$$y = 16x^2,$$

which expresses, for a body falling from rest in a vacuum, its distance y from the starting point as a function of time x, y and x being in feet and seconds, respectively. This simple expression contains all the information about the location and motion of the body at any time. Where is it after two seconds have elapsed? Just put $x = 2$ and find $y = 16(2)^2 = 64$ feet away from the starting point. Where is it after four seconds? Put $x = 4$ and find $y = 16(4)^2 = 256$ feet. How far did it go in the third and fourth seconds? Obviously, $256 - 64 = 192$ feet. What was its average velocity during this time? Clearly, $192/2 = 96$ feet per second.

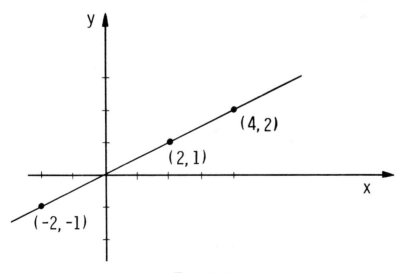

Figure A.2

Differential calculus asks a type of question harder to answer than those above: "How fast is the body traveling at time $x = 2$ seconds?" By simple arithmetic such as that just used, we can obtain close approximations to the answer by finding the average velocity between the time $x = 2$ and a time very close to $x = 2$. For example, at $x = 2$, the body is $16(2)^2 = 64$ feet from its starting place. At $x = 2.1$ it is $16(2.1)^2 = 70.56$ feet from its starting place. In 0.1 second it has therefore traveled 6.56 feet, for an average velocity of 65.6 feet/second. Now let's see what happens when the 0.1 second interval is made smaller and smaller:

TABLE A.I

Initial time, $x_1 =$	Final time, $x_2 =$	Initial location, $y_1 =$	Final location, $y_2 =$	Distance traveled, $y_2 - y_1$	Average velocity, $(y_2 - y_1)/(x_2 - x_1)$
2	2.1	64	70.56	6.56	65.6
2	2.01	64	64.6416	.6416	64.16
2	2.001	64	64.064016	.064016	64.016
2	2.0001	64	64.00640016	.00640016	64.0016
2	$2 + \epsilon$	64	$64 + 64\epsilon + 16\epsilon^2$	$64\epsilon + 16\epsilon^2$	$64 + 16\epsilon$

The last line of the table contains all the information that is contained in the earlier lines. It says that between time 2 and $2 + \epsilon$, where ϵ may be regarded as a very small time interval, the body falls $64\epsilon + 16\epsilon^2$ feet. Since this distance is covered in exactly ϵ seconds, the average velocity is $(64\epsilon + 16\epsilon^2)/\epsilon$, or $64 + 16\epsilon$ feet per second. Similarly, if we look at the falling body from time $2 - \epsilon$ to time 2, we observe that it travels $64\epsilon - 16\epsilon^2$ feet for an average speed of $64 - 16\epsilon$ feet per second:

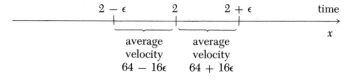

Figure A.3

Now it is intuitively clear, from Fig. A.3, that the velocity at $x = 2$, which we call the instantaneous velocity, should be so defined that it will lie between $64 - 16\epsilon$ and $64 + 16\epsilon$, no matter how small ϵ is. There is only one number that has this property, namely, 64, and we call this number the "limit of 64 + 16ε as ε approaches 0," and write it

$$\lim_{\epsilon \to 0} (64 + 16\epsilon) = 64.$$

In general, if we look at the falling body at time x, and then again at a time $x + \Delta x$, where Δx stands for an increment of time, the distance traveled in this time is called Δy and is given by

$$\Delta y = 16(x + \Delta x)^2 - 16x^2 = 32x\Delta x + 16(\Delta x)^2$$

If a distance Δy is covered in a time Δx, then the average velocity is given by

$$\frac{\Delta y}{\Delta x} = [32x\Delta x + 16(\Delta x)^2]/\Delta x = 32x + 16\Delta x.$$

Applying the above argument again, we see that we wish to define instantaneous velocity as

$$\text{instantaneous velocity} = \lim_{\Delta x \to 0} (32x + 16\,\Delta x) = 32x.$$

The answer is a function of x, since a falling body's velocity changes with time, and this formula says that the velocity in feet per second is always 32 times the number of elapsed seconds.

To be still more general, if we have a functional relationship

$$y = f(x),$$

and if we add an increment Δx to x, then an increment Δy will automatically appear on y, so that

$$y + \Delta y = f(x + \Delta x),$$

and the amount of increment Δy will be given by

$$\Delta y = f(x + \Delta x) - f(x).$$

The average rate of change of y with respect to x is, then,

$$\frac{\Delta y}{\Delta x} = \frac{f(x + \Delta x) - f(x)}{\Delta x},$$

and the instantaneous rate of change of y with respect to x, also called the *derivative* of y with respect to x, is written

$$\frac{dy}{dx} = \lim_{\Delta x \to 0} \frac{f(x + \Delta x) - f(x)}{\Delta x},$$

provided this limit exists.

When y is a linear function of x, the rate of change of y with respect to x is a constant. Specifically, if

$$y = a + bx,$$

where a and b are constants, then the constant

$$\frac{dy}{dx} = b$$

is called the slope of the line. When y is not a linear function of x, then dy/dx changes with x, that is, it is a function of x. If $y = f(x)$ is displayed graphically, then dy/dx, when it exists, is the slope of the line that is tangent to the curve for a given value of x.

Turning now to integral calculus, we find that the integral is also defined in terms of limits. In fact, the preoccupation with limits is regarded as the feature which distinguishes calculus from the more elementary branches of mathematics. The definite integral, mentioned earlier, is defined as the limit of certain sums. There are several kinds of integrals, but they are equivalent in most elementary situations. We shall discuss the one known as the Riemann integral.

Let's consider an example in which a body is moving so that its velocity varies with time as shown in Fig. A.4. That is, the curve whose graph is shown has the equation $v = f(t)$, where v and t are velocity and time, respectively. Suppose we wish to find how much distance is

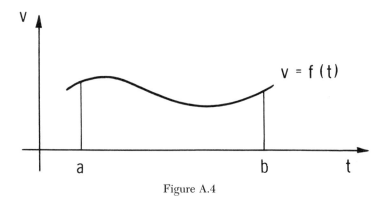

Figure A.4

covered between time a and time b. If the velocity is constant, we can simply use the fact that the distance is velocity multiplied by time, or $v(b - a)$. If the acceleration is constant the problem is still simple, for in this case the velocity is a linear function of time; thus, if v_a and v_b are the velocities at a and b, respectively, the average velocity must be $(v_a + v_b)/2$, and so the distance is given by the formula $(b - a)(v_a + v_b)/2$.

If neither the velocity nor the acceleration is constant, an approximate solution can always be found as follows:

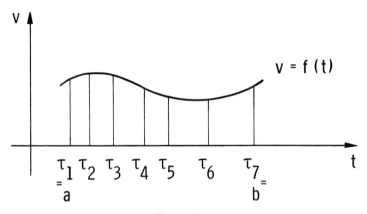

Figure A.5

Divide the time interval into several short intervals, as shown in Fig. A.5. In each of these short intervals the velocity will be almost constant. Let $\tau_1, \tau_2, \tau_3, \tau_4, \tau_5, \tau_6, \tau_7$ determine the short time intervals shown in the figure, τ_1 being at a and τ_7 at b. Let $v_1, v_2, v_3, v_4, v_5, v_6$ represent the almost-constant values of the velocity in these intervals, respectively. Then the distance covered in the first time interval is obviously approximately $v_1(\tau_2 - \tau_1)$, and so on, and the total distance is approximately

$$v_1(\tau_2 - \tau_1) + v_2(\tau_3 - \tau_2) + v_3(\tau_4 - \tau_3) + v_4(\tau_5 - \tau_4) + v_5(\tau_6 - \tau_5) + v_6(\tau_7 - \tau_6).$$

Now, it seems intuitively clear that if we make all of the intervals sufficiently small we should generally be able to come as close as we wish to finding the actual distance. It is shown in integral calculus that this is true; under certain conditions (it is sufficient for $f(t)$ to be continuous) sums found in this fashion have a unique limit as the maximum length of the time intervals is made to approach zero.

Each of the quantities $v_1, v_2, v_3, \ldots$ can be represented by a quantity $f(t_1), f(t_2), f(t_3), \ldots$, and so on, where t_1 is some number between τ_1 and τ_2, t_2 between τ_2 and τ_3, etc. The above sum then can be written as a sum of terms of the form $f(t_i)(\tau_{i+1} - \tau_i)$ or $f(t_i) \Delta t_i$, where Δt_i represents the increment $\tau_{i+1} - \tau_i$. The limit of this sum,

$$\lim \left[f(t_1)\Delta t_1 + f(t_2)\Delta t_2 + \cdots + f(t_n)\Delta t_n \right]$$

is called the integral of $f(t)$ from a to b, and is abbreviated

$$\int_a^b f(t)dt$$

where the integral sign $\int$ is a stylized S standing for summation.

Although our example used the idea that $f(t)$ was a function representing a velocity, and this gave us an integral which is a distance, it is clear that the idea of an integral is associated directly with the function $f(t)$ and does not require a physical interpretation. A geometric interpretation can be seen from the fact that each $f(t_i)(\tau_{i+1} - \tau_i)$ represents the area of a rectangle of width $\tau_{i+1} - \tau_i$ and height $f(t_i)$, and this is approximately the area under the curve and over the interval from τ_i to τ_{i+1}. In the limit, the integral is the area under the curve from a to b, as mentioned earlier.

Elementary calculus is concerned with the problem of evaluating derivatives and integrals for elementary functions. Derivatives of the elementary functions are easily found, but it turns out that integrals are generally found by an inverse differentiation process of trying to find a function given its derivative. The basis for this is known as the fundamental theorem of the calculus, which states that when an integral

$$\int_a^b f(t)dt$$

exists, if a function $F(t)$ can be found such that $f(t)$ is the derivative of $F(t)$, then the integral can be evaluated by the formula

$$\int_a^b f(t)dt = F(b) - F(a).$$

The idea involved in this fundamental theorem is apparent in the foregoing discussion, where we saw that velocity was the derivative of distance, and later that distance was the integral of velocity.

218

Certain Symbols

GREEK ALPHABET

A	α	alpha	I	ι	iota	P	ρ	rho
B	β	beta	K	κ	kappa	Σ	σ	sigma
Γ	γ	gamma	Λ	λ	lambda	T	τ	tau
Δ	δ	delta	M	μ	mu	Υ	υ	upsilon
E	ε	epsilon	N	ν	nu	Φ	φ	phi
Z	ζ	zeta	Ξ	ξ	xi	X	χ	chi
H	η	eta	O	o	omicron	Ψ	ψ	psi
Θ	θ	theta	Π	π	pi	Ω	ω	omega

In scientific notation, it has become customary to use certain symbols, as well as Greek and Roman letters, to denote specific quantities. Throughout this book such symbols have been defined in context, but the following list, intended only for reference, gives commonly accepted definitions of the letters and symbols most frequently encountered.

Δ	finite difference
θ, φ, ψ	angle
φ	work function
λ	wavelength
ν	frequency
ρ	density, or resistivity
ω	angular velocity
c	velocity of light
d	distance
E	energy, or electric field
e	charge of the electron, or the base of the natural logarithms
F	force
f	frequency
G	gravitation constant
g	acceleration of gravity
H	magnetic field intensity
h	Planck's constant
i, I	electric current
k	Boltzmann's constant
l, L	length
m, M	mass
n, N	number, especially an integer
P	pressure
p	momentum
q, Q	amount of charge
R	universal gas constant
r	radius
T	temperature
t	time
v, V	velocity, volume, voltage
∞	infinity

Certain Scientists

AVOGADRO, Count Amadeo (1776–1856) Italian physicist and chemist, who suggested in 1811 the principle that equal volumes of all gases at the same temperature contain identical numbers of molecules. Avogadro's law was much later elucidated by the Maxwell-Boltzmann law of equipartition of energy, and positively established by the experiments of J. J. Thomson, Millikan, Rutherford, and others. Avogadro's Constant is the number of molecules contained in one mole (gram-molecular weight) of a substance.

BACON, Francis (1561–1626) English philosopher and author of many important literary works. Among these is a tract in which he discusses, under the guise of mythology, the nature of matter and the limits of science. He later expanded these ideas in numerous volumes surveying the sciences and critically analyzing scientific principles and methods.

BOHR, Niels (1885–1962) Danish physicist, whose contributions to the theory of atomic structure won him the 1922 Nobel Prize in physics. Bohr applied Max Planck's quantum theory to Rutherford's nuclear concept of the atom, formulating the Bohr theory of atomic structure, and thus laying the groundwork for modern atomic physics.

BOLTZMANN, Ludwig (1844–1906) Austrian physicist, who is known especially for the Stefan-Boltzmann law of black-body radiation. Boltzmann contributed to the probability theory and the partition of energy in connection with the kinetic theory of gases.

BOYLE, Robert (1627–1691) English natural philosopher born in Ireland. In defense of his "pneumatical engine," which he developed with Robert Hooke, Boyle first enunciated the law known by his name, stating that the volume of a gas varies inversely as the pressure. This is sometimes called the Boyle-Mariotte law, although E. Mariotte did not publish his version until much later, in 1679.

BROWN, Robert (1773–1858) British botanist. While working with colloids Brown observed the phenomenon of random movement among microscopic particles, which he is said to have attributed to living organisms. With the advent of the kinetic theory, this *Brownian move-*

ment came to be associated with the thermal agitation of the suspending medium. Einstein's mathematical analysis of the problem in 1905 led to an equation which connects the motion with Boltzmann's constant, on the basis of the law of equipartition of energy.

CANTOR, Georg (1845–1918) Although his father was born in Denmark, and he himself was born in Russia, Cantor is associated with Germany, where he spent much of his life. He created the theory of sets, adding much to our understanding of concepts involving "infinity," and laid the foundations for a great deal of twentieth-century mathematics.

CHADWICK, Sir James (1891–   ) English physicist, who received the Nobel Prize in 1935 for discovering the neutron, a hitherto undetected constituent of the atom. Chadwick was knighted in 1945. He has won wide recognition for his work with radioactivity and nuclear reactions.

COMPTON, Arthur Holly (1892–1963) American physicist. For his discovery of the wavelength change of scattered x rays, known as the Compton effect, he shared the Nobel Prize for physics with C. T. R. Wilson in 1927. Compton is known for his many scientific discoveries, including total reflection of x rays and the electrical nature of cosmic rays, as well as for his work on the first atomic chain reaction.

COULOMB, Charles Augustin de (1736–1806) French physicist, noted for his experiments on friction and for his researches in electricity and magnetism. He formulated Coulomb's law of the forces existing between charged bodies, and the coulomb, a unit of electrical quantity, is named for him.

CROOKES, Sir William (1832–1919) English physicist and chemist. As early as 1886, Crookes contended that elements contain atoms of different atomic weights, and he devised a spiral model of the periodic system. His pioneer studies in rarefied gases led to his observing the dark space which bears his name.

DICKE, Robert Henry (1916–   ) American physicist, noted for his contributions to scientific theory in the areas of microwave radio and measurement of thermal radiation from the sun and the moon at microwave frequencies. His researches have also included inelastic scattering of protons, optically induced polarization, and gravitation.

DIRAC, Paul Adrien Maurice (1902–   ) British mathematical physicist in the field of atomic structure. In 1933 Dirac was awarded the Nobel Prize (jointly with Erwin Schrödinger) for his pioneer work in the quantum mechanics of the atom. He is co-discoverer of the Fermi-Dirac statistics, and also pioneered in developing the quantum theory of radiation.

DOPPLER, Christian Johann (1803–1853) Austrian physicist. Although Doppler's earliest writings were on mathematics, his name is primarily associated with his work in physics. Doppler's principle, first enunciated in 1842, is applied to the motion of stars in the line of sight, and used for the discovery of double stars. The Doppler effect is a characteristic of both sound waves and light waves.

EDDINGTON, Sir Arthur Stanley (1882–1944) British astronomer, the father of dynamical stellar astronomy. Eddington did significant work on the first observational confirmation of Einstein's general theory of relativity. Later he made the major discovery of the relationship between the masses and the luminosities of stars. His interest in the nature of diffuse matter in interstellar space has had a profound effect on astronomical research.

EINSTEIN, Albert (1879–1955) Mathematician and theoretical physicist, born in Germany. Einstein became a Swiss citizen in his youth, and in 1940 he was naturalized as a citizen of the United States. Each of three papers, published when he was twenty-six, became the source of a new branch of physics. Although Einstein is probably most famous for his theory of relativity, he also did significant work on the photoelectric effect, for which he was awarded the Nobel Prize in 1922, as well as on the theory of Brownian movement, emission and absorption of radiation, and particle statistics.

FARADAY, Michael (1791–1867) English physicist and chemist, whose greatest contributions were in the fields of electricity and magnetism. His discoveries of electromagnetic induction, the magnetization of light, and diamagnetism are especially noteworthy. He was also responsible for advances in the study of electrolysis, the liquefaction of gases, and many other areas of physics and chemistry.

FERMI, Enrico (1901–1954) Italian physicist, who became a United States citizen in 1939. Fermi is noted for his studies in nuclear physics and was awarded the Nobel Prize in 1938 for his research on artificial radioactive substances. His investigations have included the quantum theory of radiation, the magnetic movements of nuclei, and the structure of the atom. Fermi was the discoverer of element 93, neptunium, and was one of the leading scientists who contributed to the development of the atomic bomb.

FISHER, Sir Ronald Aylmer (1890–1926) English mathematician and geneticist, who founded the science of design of experiments and made important contributions to it, including the concept of randomization.

GAUSS, Karl Friedrich (1777–1855) German mathematician, often classed with Newton and Archimedes as one of the three greatest mathematicians of all time. A famous child prodigy, he eventually influenced strongly almost all areas of mathematics including geometry, number theory, functions of a complex variable, infinite processes, algebra, the theory of errors, physics, and astronomy.

GAY-LUSSAC, Joseph Louis (1778–1850) French chemist and physicist, noted for his researches on chemical combinations, iodine, and cyanogen. He enunciated the law that bears his name, stating that gases combine with each other in simple definite proportions.

GEIGER, Hans (1882–1947) German physicist, who is known for his investigations in atomic theory, radioactivity, and cosmic rays. The Geiger-Müller counter (often called simply the Geiger counter) is named for him and his colleague, W. Müller.

GOLAY, Marcel Jules Edouard (1902–   ) American physicist, born in Switzerland, whose major work has been in the areas of acoustics, infrared, communications, nuclear magnetic resonance, and gas chromatography. The Golay pneumatic cell, named for him, is a small transparent cell containing gas which is used to detect radiation.

HEISENBERG, Werner (1901–   ) German physicist whose matrix theory of quantum mechanics is an important factor in the general quantum theory. He was awarded the 1932 Nobel Prize in physics for this contribution and for his investigations of hydrogen.

HERTZ, Heinrich (1857–1894) German physicist, known especially for his discovery of the electric waves of large amplitude which have been utilized in wireless telegraphy. He also did significant investigation of the relation between electricity and light, and the properties of electrical discharges in rarefied gases.

HITTORF, Johann Wilhelm (1824–1914) German physicist, who pioneered in the study of cathode rays. His researches in the migration of ions during electrolysis and his measurements of relative velocities of different ions pulled through water by an electric field led to later ionic theories.

JOHNSON, John Bertrand (1887–   ) American physicist, born in Sweden. Johnson is noted for his researches in infrared, gas ionization, cathode ray tubes, and noise in circuits. His investigations also include supersonics in liquids and secondary emission.

JOULE, James Prescott (1818–1889) English physicist, known for his researches in the mechanical equivalent of heat. These studies led to a series of experiments on the equivalence of heat and energy. The joule, a physical unit of work equal to ten million ergs, is named for him. Joule considered the acquisition of exact quantitative data of primary importance in scientific research. In studying the relations between electrical, mechanical, and chemical effects, he discovered the first law of thermodynamics.

KELVIN, Lord (William Thomson) (1824–1907) British physicist, born in Ireland. Kelvin was recognized as one of the greatest physicists of his time. Influenced by Joule's theory of heat, he proposed an absolute scale of temperature independent of any thermometric substance. A few years later, Kelvin reconciled the work of Sadi Carnot with that of Count Rumford, Sir Humphry Davy, J. R. Mayer, and Joule; his resulting dynamical theory of heat and the fundamental principle of conservation of energy commanded universal acceptance. At the same time he first stated briefly his principle of dissipation of energy, the second law of thermodynamics. Kelvin's contributions to thermodynamics are considered of primary importance, but he was also responsible for significant advances in many other areas of research.

MACH, Ernst (1838–1916) Austrian physicist and philosopher, whose work in both fields greatly influenced twentieth-century thought. Most scientists now share Mach's view that any statement in natural science is inadmissible unless it is empirically verifiable. His criteria of verifiability were so rigorous, however, that he rejected not only such concepts as that of the ether, and of absolute space and time, but even opposed introducing atoms and molecules into physical theory. Mach's criticism along these lines of Newton's system cleared the way for Einstein's theory of relativity.

MARIOTTE, Edmé (1620–1684) French physicist, who made many discoveries in hydrodynamics, did significant research on the nature of color, and discovered the "blind spot" of the human eye. Mariotte is sometimes credited (Mariotte's law) with originating the principle previously discovered by Robert Boyle and usually known as Boyle's law.

MAXWELL, James Clerk (1831–1879) British physicist, born in Scotland. At the age of fifteen, Maxwell made the first of his many scientific contributions, and by the time he was eighteen his singular genius was becoming apparent. In his extraordinary investigations, which included electricity, magnetism, elastic solids, color perception, and the kinetic theory of gases, Maxwell was not only the experimenter but often the mathematician as well. Of his many great contributions, the most significant dealt with the physical theory of electromagnetism.

MICHELSON, Albert Abraham (1852–1931) American physicist, born in Germany. Following his graduation from the U. S. Naval Academy, Michelson stayed on as instructor of chemistry and physics. He resigned from the Navy in 1881. While teaching in Cleveland, Ohio, Michelson invented his interferometer with which he conducted his celebrated experiments on the velocity of light. Honored by many learned societies, Michelson's most important award was the Nobel Prize in 1907.

MILLIKAN, Robert Andrews (1868–1953) American physicist, whose first outstanding contribution was his famous oil-drop experiment, an accurate measurement of the charge of the electron, and proof that this charge is a definite quantity and therefore a fundamental constant. He later provided equally skillful experimental verification of Einstein's photoelectric equation, and the evaluation of Planck's constant. Millikan's researches also dealt with cosmic rays, the mysterious radiation from outer space. In 1923, he was awarded the Nobel Prize.

NEWTON, Sir Issac (1642–1727) English mathematician and natural philosopher. There is no example of greater achievement in the history of science than that of Newton, who at twenty-three made three fundamental discoveries: the method of calculus, which is the basis for much of modern mathematics; the spectral composition of light and the fundamentals of optics; and the law of universal gravitation and the basic laws of mechanics.

NYQUIST, H. (1889–   ) Born in Sweden. As communications engineer at American Telephone and Telegraph Company and Bell Telephone Laboratories, Nyquist has made significant contributions to telegraphy. He postulated the theory of thermal agitation of electricity in conductors —the Johnson-Nyquist noise.

ØRSTED, Hans Christian (1777–1851) Danish physicist, especially noted for his discovery of electromagnetism.

PEARSON, Karl (1857–1936) English mathematician, who devoted his career to biometry, the science of measurement of life. He founded the journal *Biometrika*, and through it made many important contributions to statistics.

PLANCK, Max (1857–1947) German theoretical physicist, who made the significant discovery that energy exists in quantized form. From this premise, he derived the universal Law of Radiation in 1901. Professor of Physics at Kiel and at Berlin, Planck was the author of such classic works on theoretical physics as *Theory of Heat Radiation*. In 1918, he was awarded the Nobel Prize in physics.

POISSON, Siméon Denis (1781–1840) French mathematician, who studied medicine but gave it up in favor of mathematics. Poisson did important work on the application of mathematics to physics, particularly to electrostatics and magnetism. In the field of pure mathematics, he made his greatest contribution with his work on definite integrals and Fourier's series. This paved the way for the researches of Dirichlet and Riemann.

RIEMANN, Georg Friedrich Bernhard (1826–1866) German mathematician and mathematical physicist. Riemann lived a short life of poverty and poor health, but he made important contributions to the theory of functions of a complex variable, and his "Riemannian geometry" helped lead to the development of Einstein's theory of relativity.

ROENTGEN, Wilhelm Konrad (1845–1923) German physicist, who discovered x rays. He was professor of physics at Giessen and Würzburg, and in 1901, he won the Nobel Prize in physics.

RUTHERFORD, Ernest (1871–1937) British physicist, born in New Zealand. Rutherford was the first to discover the components of radioactive emission (called alpha, beta, and gamma rays). From his study of alpha rays, he derived the first successful model of the atom in 1912, and discovered the disintegration of nuclei by bombardment with alpha particles. He was awarded the Nobel prize in 1908.

SCHOTTKY, Walter (1886–   ) Schottky, the son of a German mathematician, discovered laws governing the transit of electrons between electrodes in the presence of space charge. He also invented the screen-grid tube, and derived the shot noise formula, known as the Schottky effect.

SCHRÖDINGER, Erwin (1887–   ) German physicist, noted for having introduced wave mechanics, an advanced form of the quantum theory, which made it possible to compute parameters and physical characteristics of the atom. He won the Nobel Prize with Paul Dirac in 1933.

SEEBECK, Thomas Johann (1770–1831) German physicist who discovered thermoelectricity and its application to the measurement of temperature. Seebeck worked with Goethe on the theory of color, and pioneered in polarization experiments.

STEFAN, Josef (1835–1893) From a critical evaluation of radiation measurements, Stefan derived what was then the empirical relationship that the power emitted by a black body is proportional to the fourth power of its absolute temperature. The law was later derived theoretically by Boltzmann.

Stokes, Sir George Gabriel (1819–1903) British mathematician and physicist, Professor of Physics at Cambridge, who discovered the law that fluorescent light is shifted toward the red with respect to the primary radiation. Stokes was also the discoverer of the relation between the force and the velocity of bodies moving in fluids.

Thomson, Sir Joseph John (1856–1940) British physicist who determined the ratio of mass and charge of the electron by the deflection of cathode rays in combined electric and magnetic fields.

Townes, C. H. (1915–   ) American physicist, Professor of Physics at Columbia University and Provost at Massachusettes Institute of Technology, who is noted for his original concept of the maser principle, and for his pioneer work on masers and lasers.

Townsend, J. S. E. (1868–   ) Born in Galway, Ireland, Townsend became Professor of Physics at Oxford in 1901, and held this post until 1941. He is noted for discovering the critical conditions under which a spark discharge is initiated.

Weber, Wilhelm (1804–1890) German physicist, founder of the electrical unit system, who was the first to realize that the relationship between electric and magnetic units contains the velocity of light. Weber was the inventor of a sensitive galvanometer.

The Authors

RUSSELL Fox joined the staff of the Westinghouse Research Laboratories twenty years ago. He is at present manager of the Physics Department, Westinghouse Research and Development Center.

Born in Richmond, Virginia, he attended high school in Hampton, graduated *summa cum laude* from Hampden-Sydney College, and received his M.S. and his Ph.D. in physics from the University of Virginia. He is a member of Phi Beta Kappa and Sigma Xi.

Dr. Fox is also a member of numerous national and local scientific societies, and is current Chairman of the National Mass Spectrometry Society. He is the author of more than forty scientific papers dealing with basic studies of ionization processes by electrons in atoms and molecules.

Married and the father of three teen-agers, he still manages to find time not only for an active role in civic affairs but for his favorite hobbies, which include duplicate bridge, gardening, and classical music. Both as a lecturer and an author, he also devotes a good deal of time to interpreting scientific subjects for young people.

In speaking of his choice of a career in science, Dr. Fox says, "I was fortunate in having physics teachers in high school and in college, who presented the subject in such an interesting and challenging manner that they were directly responsible for my choosing science as a career. I particularly appreciate the encouragement I received from Professor T. E. Gilmer, my physics professor at Hampden-Sydney College."

Max Garbuny, full-time Consulting Physicist at the Westinghouse Research Laboratories, first joined the staff in 1946 as a research physicist, and later became manager of the Optical Physics section. An experienced teacher with a reputation for wit and infectious humor, Dr. Garbuny has lectured at Princeton University and, since 1959, has conducted a series of short summer courses at the University of California in Los Angeles.

Born and educated in Germany, he received degrees of Dipl. Ing. and Dr. Ing. at Institute of Technology in Berlin. Although he studied English in high school, he recalls that he first discovered he could really understand and enjoy the language when he started reading a detective story by Edgar Wallace and couldn't stop until daylight.

Dr. Garbuny came to the United States when he was twenty-five and he now comments, "In Germany, I was considered much too young to marry at that age. In crossing the Atlantic, my status changed within fourteen days; in this country I was not only old enough, but I began to suspect I might be *too* old." He solved his problem by finding an attractive wife, and they now have three lively daughters.

His interest in physics was aroused at an early age when he read a booklet on the nature of electricity. Later, he was delighted to learn that the pursuit of his interest in science was quite compatible with earning a livelihood. The author of numerous scientific articles and patents in such fields as optical radiation physics, Dr. Garbuny has recently started writing books, in the hope of sharing with others his own enthusiasm for scientific investigation.

 ROBERT HOOKE, manager of the Mathematics Department of Westinghouse Research Laboratories, spent the first ten years of his career teaching mathematics at North Carolina State College and University of the South. He then went to Washington to work with the Operations Evaluation Group, Department of the Navy, and from there to Princeton University's Analytical Research Group, before joining the research staff at Westinghouse in 1954. One of Dr. Hooke's distinguished contributions is the theoretical work for the OPCON control, for which Westinghouse received the AAAS Industrial Achievement Award for 1958.

Born in Chattanooga, Tennessee, he attended the University of North Carolina, graduating in 1938 and receiving his M.A. the following year. In 1942, he received his Ph.D. from Princeton University. In the meantime, he had married and his two sons are now in college, studying mathematics and physics.

Although he likes all sports, Dr. Hooke is especially enthusiastic about baseball. He enjoys reading and philately, and his interest in word puzzles led him to accept the 1961–62 presidency of the National Puzzler's League.

Dr. Hooke says he thinks he decided on a career in mathematics at the age of twelve, when it began to become clear that mathematics contained something besides arithmetic.

For Further Reading

Part One

Born, Max. *Einstein's Theory of Relativity.* Translated by Henry L. Brose. New York: E. P. Dutton & Co., 1922.

Møller, Christian. *The Theory of Relativity.* New York: Oxford University Press, 1952.

Part Two

American Association for the Advancement of Science, Section on Engineering. *Systems of Units; National and International Aspects.* (Publication Number 57) Baltimore, Md.: Horn Shafer Co., 1959.

Churchman, Charles W. and Ratoosh, Philburn (eds.). *Measurement: Definitions and Theories.* (A symposium of the American Association for the Advancement of Science) New York: John Wiley and Sons, Inc., 1959.

Wilson, Edgar B., Jr. *An Introduction to Scientific Research.* New York: McGraw-Hill Book Co., Inc., 1952.

Dixon, Wilfrid J. and Massey, F. J., Jr. *Introduction to Statistical Analysis.* New York: McGraw-Hill Book Co., Inc., 1957.

Cox, D. R. *Planning of Experiments.* New York: John Wiley and Sons, Inc., 1958.

Huff, Darrell and Geis, Irving. *How to Lie with Statistics.* New York: Norton Publishing Co., 1954.

Moroney, M. J. *Facts from Figures.* Baltimore: Penguin Books, Inc., 1951.

Wallis, Wilson A. and Roberts, Harry V. *Statistics: A New Approach.* (Free Press of Glencoe, Inc., Glencoe, Illinois.) New York: Macmillan Co., 1956.

Halmos, Paul R. *Measure Theory.* New York: van Nostrand, 1950.

Munroe, Marshall E. *Introduction to Measure and Integration.* Reading, Mass.: Addison-Wesley, 1953.

Hooke, Robert. *Introduction to Scientific Inference.* San Francisco: Holden-Day, 1963.

Part Three

Ruch, Theodore C. and Fulton, John F. (eds.). *Medical Physiology and Biophysics* (18th ed.). Philadelphia: W. B. Saunders Co., 1960.

Best, Charles H. and Taylor, Norman B. *Physiological Basis of Medical Practice* (7th ed.). Baltimore: Williams and Wilkins Co., 1961.

Strong, John, et al. *Procedures in Experimental Physics.* Englewood Cliffs, N.J.: Prentice-Hall, Inc., 1956.

International Instruments and Measurement Conference. Fifth. Stockholm, 1960. Proceedings. *Instruments and Measurements.* Koch, H. T. von and Ljungberg, G. (eds.). New York: Academic Press, 1961.

Bachman, Charles H. *Physics, A Descriptive Interpretation.* New York: John Wiley and Sons, Inc., 1955.

Draper, Charles S., et al. *Instrument Engineering:* Vol. I, Fundamentals, 1952; Vol. II, Mathematics: Methods for associating mathematical solutions with common forms, 1953; Vol. III, Part I, Measurement Systems: Applications of the instrument engineering method. New York: McGraw-Hill Book Co., Inc., 1955.

Conference on Vacuum Microbalance Techniques, 1960. Fort Monmouth, N.J. Sponsored by Institute for Exploratory Research, U.S. Army Signal Research and Development Laboratory Proceedings. *Vacuum Microbalance Techniques:* Vol. I, Editor, Katz, Max J. New York: Plenum Press, Inc., 1961.

Part Four

Schrödinger, Erwin. *What is Life?* New York: Macmillan Co., 1945.

Born, Max. *Atomic Physics,* 7th ed. New York: Hafner Publishing Co., 1962. (Rev. by the author in coll. with R. J. Blin-Stoyle from the orig. tr. of John Dougall. Blackie and Son, London.)

Laundau, L. D. and Lifshitz, E. M. *Statistical Physics.* Reading, Mass.: Addison-Wesley Publishing Co., Inc., 1958.

Schottky, W. "Über spontane Stromschwankungen in verschiedenen Elektrizitätsleitern." *Annalen der Physik,* V. 57, p. 541–567, 1918.

Johnson, J. B. "Thermal agitation of electricity in conductors." *Physical review,* V. 32, p. 97–109. 1928.

Nyquist, H. "Thermal agitation of electric charge in conductors." *Physical Review,* V. 32, p. 110–114. 1928.

Jones, R. C. "Performance of Detectors for visible and infrared radiation." *Advances in Electronics,* V. 5, p. 62–96. 1954.

——— "Quantum efficiency of detectors for visible and infrared radiation." *Advances in Electronics,* V. 11, p. 87–183. 1959.

Part Five

Cohen, E. Richard, Crowe, K. M., Dumond, J. W. M. *Fundamental Constants of Physics.* New York: John Wiley and Sons, Inc., 1957.

Shamos, Morris H. *Great Experiments in Physics.* New York: Holt, Rinehart and Winston, Inc., 1959.

Born, Max. *The Restless Universe,* 2nd rev. ed. tr. by Winifred M. Deans. New York: Dover Publications, Inc., 1951.

Massey, Sir Harrie S. W. *The New Age in Physics.* New York: Harper and Row, Publishers, 1960.

Millikan, Robert A. *Autobiography.* New York: Prentice-Hall, Inc., 1950.

Thomson, Sir Joseph John. *Recollections and Reflections.* Toronto: Macmillan Co., 1937.

Dicke, Robert Henry. "Gravitation, an Enigma." *American Scientist,* V. 47, p. 25–40. 1959.

Brans, C. and Dicke, Robert Henry. Mach's Principle and a Relativistic Theory of Gravitation. *Physical Review,* V. 124, p. 225–235. 1961.

Planck, Max K. E. L. *The Theory of Heat Radiation* (tr. by Morton Masius from the German 2nd ed., 1913) 2nd ed. New York: Dover Publications, Inc., 1959.

Index

201437

DATE DUE

MAY 18 73			
OL 11 UN			
AP 10 '86			
GAYLORD			PRINTED IN U..S.A.